THE CHESAPEAKE AND POTOMAC TELEPHONE
WESTERN BELL TELEPHONE COMP
ERN NEW ENGLAND TELEPHONE COMPANY THE
MARYLAND CINCINNATI BELL, INC. SOUTHWES
ORATORIES NEW YORK TELEPHONE COMPANY
OF VIRGINIA MICHIGAN BELL TELEPHONE COMPAN
APH COMPANY WESTERN ELECTRIC NEW JERSEY B
OTOMAC TELEPHONE COMPANY OF WEST VIRGINIA
HWEST BELL TELEPHONE COMPANY THE BELL TE
TELEPHONE AND TELEGRAPH COMPANY WISCON
AND TELEGRAPH COMPANY BELL TELEPHONE COM
AMOND STATE TELEPHONE COMPANY SOUTH CENTR
HONE COMPANY NEW ENGLAND TELEPHONE & TEL
C TELEPHONE COMPANY THE OHIO BELL TELEPH
PANY AMERICAN TELEPHONE AND TELEGRAPH COM
MPANY THE CHESAPEAKE AND POTOMAC TELEP
SOUTHWESTERN BELL TELEPHONE COMPANY BELL
OMPANY THE CHESAPEAKE AND POTOMAC TELEP
HONE COMPANY THE MOUNTAIN STATES TELEPHO
EW JERSEY BELL TELEPHONE COMPANY THE CHES
EST VIRGINIA INDIANA BELL TELEPHONE COMPANY
HE BELL TELEPHONE COMPANY OF PENNSYLVANIA S
PANY WISCONSIN TELEPHONE COMPANY THE PA
EPHONE COMPANY OF NEVADA LONG LINES DEP
SOUTH CENTRAL BELL TELEPHONE COMPANY ILLIN
EPHONE & TELEGRAPH COMPANY THE CHESAPEA
L TELEPHONE COMPANY NORTHWESTERN BELL TEL
EGRAPH COMPANY THE SOUTHERN NEW ENGLAND T
MAC TELEPHONE COMPANY OF MARYLAND CINCIN
OMPANY BELL TELEPHONE LABORATORIES NEW YOR
TOMAC TELEPHONE COMPANY OF VIRGINIA MICHIGA
S TELEPHONE AND TELEGRAPH COMPANY WESTERN
THE CHESAPEAKE AND POTOMAC TELEPHONE COM
COMPANY PACIFIC NORTHWEST BELL TELEPHONE C
SYLVANIA SOUTHERN BELL TELEPHONE AND TELEGR
HE PACIFIC TELEPHONE AND TELEGRAPH COMPANY
P9-DNN-291

THE TEL

TELEPHONE BOOK

BELL, WATSON, VAIL AND

MERICAN LIFE, 1876-1976

H.M. BOETTINGER   RIVERWOOD PUBLISHERS LTD

CROTON-ON-HUDSON, N.Y.

SPECIAL PHOTOGRAPHY BY RICHARD A. STEINBERG

DESIGN BY RAY RIPPER

FOR SHIRLEY

PROJECT STAFF

Art & Production Director: Ray Ripper
Design Associate: Janet Zuckerman
Copy: Dorothy M. Stearn
Photographic Research Assistant: Daniel Kaufman
Historical Photographic Research Consultants: Adrian Rosen and Melvin Gray of The Bettmann Archive.
Typographic Consultants: Frederick Lev and Steven Bachleda of Typographic Art Inc.
Paper Consultant: Thomas Ferguson of Bulkley Dunton Linde Lathrop
Photographic Processing: Sam Weinstein and Zvi Caspi of Colorlab
Assistant to the Publisher: Anita Marshall
Printing Coordinator: H.C. Ohser
Color separations, printing and binding by the W.A. Krueger Company Brookfield and New Berlin, Wisconsin

THE TELEPHONE BOOK was conceived and produced by Gerald Stearn, *Publisher*

RIVERWOOD PUBLISHERS LIMITED
CROTON-ON-HUDSON, NEW YORK 10520

CONTENTS

"Weavers of Speech" first appeared in a Bell System national magazine advertisement in December, 1915.

INTRODUCTION AND APOLOGY

This book is not a biography, a detailed history or a complicated, scholarly study. Instead, it is my attempt to tell the story of the colorful personalities, social conflicts and forces set in motion a century ago, and the role they played in shaping the institution established by the invention of the telephone. I have worked with that creation — the Bell System — and know it from the inside, perhaps, as well as anyone.

What follows is my attempt to answer certain questions: What, if anything, does the telephone mean to America? Why is it worthwhile to know about the telephone in American Life?

The Bell System is an important social instrument, a formidable economic presence, a responder to public demands, complaints and fears and, finally, an engine of technological change.

As it enters the second century of its life, this may not be a bad time for one of its "family" — admittedly a somewhat eccentric member — to set down interpretations and reflections on the origins and character of a unique aggregation of human effort, the people who created it and the nation which encouraged its growth and pursuit of excellence.

There are now about one million persons employed in the Bell System, over a hundred and fifty thousand of its veterans on pensions, and a hundred thousand new recruits coming to its ranks each year. I hope that my excursion of discovery may stimulate reflections on their own experiences and future careers.

New York 1976.

H. M. B.

"The Spirit of Service." Intrepid lineman Angus A. MacDonald was photographed during the great Blizzard of 1888 patrolling the New York-Boston-Maine telephone line. This famous drawing, based on the photograph, came to symbolize the dedication of Bell System workers. MacDonald died in 1958 at 94.

AMERICAN TELEPHONE & TELEGRAPH CO.
BELL SYSTEM
AND ASSOCIATED COMPANIES

CHAPTER

1

1

The telephone is so much a part of our lives that use of it is habitual, not conscious. In the history of invention and technology, no other device can be used — in safety — with such total disregard of the *thing* itself. Most inventions of that flood whose tide rose in the Industrial Revolution have been amplifications and extensions of man's strength or enhancement of a single sense. Whether steam engines, textile machinery, railroads, ships, machine tools, telegraphs, chemicals, mining equipment, telescopes, microscopes, metallurgy, automobiles or the household appliances now considered essential for life even at poverty levels, some transmutation of power or special training in their use is required. All can cause accidents to their operators or bystanders. The telephone is an outstanding exception. Its uniquely phenomenal growth and pervasiveness in our lives can in large measure be ascribed to its total ease and safety of use.

Most inventions alter the linear, reciprocating motions of the human body (based on extension and contraction of muscles) into mechanically more efficient rotary actions such as circular saws, trench-digging machines, concrete mixers or grindstones. (The classic reciprocating-to-rotary motion converter is the *crank* — one of the basic inventions of our culture.) But the *telephone* accepts the native, natural sounds of a human voice, silently translates them into forms suitable for electrical processes — and then delivers a faithful replica of the original voice directly to a listener's ear. During early demonstrations of the telephone, audiences gave standing ovations to the "magic" of transmitting a conversation between two Choctaw Indians who were introduced to the instruments for the first time. We smile at the scientific naiveté of those

OUR SIXTH-AND-A-HALF SENSE

frock-coated and crinolined crowds. We are habituated to the telephone as an extension of ourselves. Yet we may still wonder at the genie who faithfully sped the expressions of *any* human voice with the velocity of light.

The name itself, derived from the two Greek words for *far* (tele) and *voice* (phone), is found in the vocabulary of nearly every language possessing a written literature. (Exceptions like the German *Fernsprecher* (far speaker), are the result of those rashes of linguistic insularity which sweep over even mature nations from time to time.)

There are about 300 million "phones" in daily use throughout the world, from Pitcairn Island's 31, to 150 million in the United States alone. They have altered, in a thousand, subtle ways, the daily lives of those who use them. Telephones sit, unremarked and unremarkable, in alcoves of luxurious penthouses and the corners of rural cabins, on the desks of heads of state and the walls of shanty offices. Every day mankind, in unnumbered interactions, struggles through its labors, using the energies of a silent servant who has become so unobtrusive that it totally blends into the background of living.

From 1950 to 1975, over two and one-third trillion — 2,300,000,000,000 — telephone calls went through Bell System central offices.

It all began with the strange, driven behavior of two of the most improbable inventors our world has ever seen. Seldom have two less likely types created a silent revolution promising such an extraordinary social impact. This is their glory: *What they gave us 100 years ago is now so taken-for-granted that we become aware of our dependence only when it does not work — when the*

A field telephone used to summon aid in case of fire, Heber Canyon, Utah, 1912.

"servant" *becomes ill* — or when we find ourselves in regions still untouched by its necessity. The army of scientists, engineers, operators, craftsmen and managers, whose minds and muscles are dedicated to its continuous operation, embrace as their criteria of excellence the hope that "no one noticed what we did." This peculiar, though traditional, motivation betokens a triumph of duty. It also creates challenges of enormous scale when public understanding of a seemingly overwhelming problem *is* essential.

Over the years, countless variations and design adaptations have allowed persons suffering all kinds of handicaps — blindness, deafness, loss of a larynx or deep paralysis — the pleasures of near-normal contacts with their fellows. Certain forms of stuttering disappear when those afflicted converse by telephone and no one really knows the reasons for the cure. Infants barely able to crawl are taught to twirl a dial marked "Operator" for use in emergencies. Lists of numbers useful or vital for assistance are placed nearby, in kitchens and bedrooms, ready for summoning instantly every kind of aid. Lonely people, smothered by a city's indifference, randomly dial numbers hoping for a moment's comfort from a sympathetic voice.

When asked how he graded his responses to problems, one eminent politician said, "If it's routine, I write an official a letter; if really important, I phone him; only for averting disaster do I visit him." Notice the social change implied, almost an inversion from nineteenth century practice.

Of course, the return to oral discourse (older than Neolithic villages) and neglect of written modes have caused a melancholy decline in personal letter writing skills and volume. Schoolchildren and debutantes are taught "telephone etiquette," yet often cannot frame a paragraph. Histories and biographies of the future will mark the change, for only in unusual cases will private conversations of value and insight be available to scholars. The telephone has made invisible some vital information.

Another behavioral characteristic peculiar to our era is that produced by the insistence of a ringing telephone bell. Faced by a long line of customers at her counter, a clerk will turn from them to give sales information to a telephone inquiry. At home, or in a meeting, most persons will drop whatever they are doing and almost compulsively answer an interrupting call. This mysterious charm of the unknown, the impulse to know the news — good or bad — which spices and occasionally poisons our lives, offers modern dramatists a splendid device to introduce discontinuities and developments in a plot — at less expense and with greater speed than that available to Shakespeare. Where the Bard needed a brace or two of soldiers, gravediggers, travelers or officials to bring news of foreign parts or events, today's theatrical scenes often have violent discussions between protagonists suddenly interrupted by a telephone bell — and *everyone in the audience expects someone to answer it immediately.* Novels of suspense and espionage cannot do without the instrument. In the novel and movie, *The Day of the Jackal,* the entire story is built on a network of telephone calls among a score of characters and across the frontiers of six nations.

"The telephone began as a novelty, became a necessity and is now regarded as an absolute right". *Marshall McLuhan*

When the plans were drawn for rebuilding the bombed-out House of Commons and shaping it into a modern, efficient structure, Prime Minister Winston Churchill asked the members whether they wished to alter the procedures and

"This is a recording. When you hear 'beep,' please leave your message. Beep."

*"A grasshopper sitting on a railroad track,
Sing Polly-woolly-doodle all the day;
He sneezed so hard he broke his back,
Sing Polly-woolly-doodle all the day."*

Drawing by T.S.; © 1971 The New Yorker Magazine, Inc.

Beacon Hill, Boston, in the 1880's.

"New" office workers (1890's).

forms of Parliament. Silence. He then said, "Very well. Then we will restore the House exactly as it stood, for first we shape our buildings, and then our buildings shape us." So also with this most innocent and unobtrusive invention, which began as a toy, acquired status as a luxury, became a comfort, and is now such a necessity that families on welfare are allowed to have their telephones paid for by the state. We shaped it — together with the systems designed to further its convenience and necessity to us — and now it shapes our lives, in ways we never imagine.

With a phone at our side, we can call nearly anyone. In business, education, the military, government and the church, we can call with little anxiety powerful persons in a complex hierarchy. They usually accept the calls, and the caller demands an answer. Both parties would be uncomfortable in an actual confrontation. The element of awe natural to — and often

designed into — a structure of powerful relationships is subtly undermined in a generation. Leadership now must be founded on real knowledge rather than conferred status. Power loses its remoteness and becomes accountable.

Another aspect of social change triggered by this invention is the presence of women in offices. Together with the typewriter, the telephone created an entering wedge which razed the barriers to their employment in clerical domains. In advertisements at the turn of the century, "typewriter" and "telephonist" were prestige positions. Fashion responded by producing "appropriate" clothing, like the shirtwaist and blouse, for those new women "going to business." Few devices are so well matched to the needs and style of women. The instrument seems particularly suited to their voice range and timbre.

Over three million women have been hired by the Bell System in 100 years: 1876-1976.

Some Puritans were so alarmed at the possibilities inherent in secret, amorous conversation of young girls that these worthies suggested laws prohibiting telephones in bedrooms. A blizzard of popular music, beginning with lines in a *Pinafore* quartet, developed the opportunities lurking in love-at-a-distance. Titles like *Hello, Central, Give Me Heaven,* and *All Alone by the Telephone* exploited new dimensions in romance.

"Puritanism — the haunting fear that someone, somewhere, may be happy". H. L. Mencken

All such events underscore the central characteristic of telephone communication — a direct person-to-person conversation conducted in privacy, with no record of words and thoughts available to others. This foundation for utter freedom of expression caused Stalin to veto Trotsky's plans for development of a modern telephone system soon after the Russian Revolution. "It will unmake our work. No greater instrument for counter-revolution and conspiracy can be imagined" was his reported comment. Controlled broadcasting and a subservient press are the natural allies of the totalitarian mind. These are essentially one-way techniques: a powerful message-giver lectures the masses, with little or no critical response anticipated. The telephone is the ally of democratic societies, where *individuals* safely share ideas, opinions and reactions with one another, however heretical or unorthodox. Stalin was right: an open, efficient telephone system is a barrier to the dictatorship of the mind.

This urge (and habit) for free expression in oral discourse is the bedrock of telephone utility. In America, it explains the legitimate outrage of all telephone users at perversions like wiretapping and seizure of call records, no matter what the reason. The telephone companies profoundly understand this and have rightfully and vigorously opposed all efforts to undermine the integrity of their service. However difficult it may make law enforcement, telephonic freedom is simply too precious a right to imperil. In countries where wiretapping and surveillance are common and expected, widespread use and growth of telephones have not occurred. One of the first acts of a president of France, eager to establish a new relationship between his government and its citizens, was to abolish the official wiretapping headquarters. This act led to popular acclaim. Thus deep wellsprings of trust are involved when a society embraces telephone conversation as a habit.

One measure of value for anything we possess is the sense of deprivation accompanying its loss. We take health for granted until disease strikes, become newly sensitive to the beauty of voices and music at the onset of deafness, are unaware of muscles until we overstrain them, and appreciate all the virtues of friends only when death takes them from us. So too with that habitual extension of our senses, the telephone. When it is taken out by a thunderstorm, when unusual peaks in usage cause system breakdowns, when delays occur in installing service in a new home or business — those affected feel a deep sense of outrage. "Community" and "communications" share the same etymological root. They are linked in our consciousness. When we are isolated by a communications breakdown, we are truly isolated from the security, involvement and mutual dependence of our community. This awareness has produced in those who provide personal communications an attitude, inexplicable to cynics, known as the "spirit of service." This "spirit" is thoroughly real to those who experience it, calling forth responses ranging from acts of true heroism in disasters, to doing dirty jobs deep in the muck of flooded

"And so, Comrades, rush right down to your local commissary and buy a box without delay."

Drawing by Dana Fradon; © 1953 The New Yorker Magazine, Inc.

Sheet music covers. The telephone enters popular culture around 1900.

16

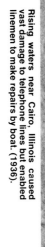

Traffic operators continue communications after a 1926 fire by using a public telephone mounted on a utility pole.

Rising waters near Cairo, Illinois caused vast damage to telephone lines but enabled linemen to make repairs by boat. (1936).

Angus MacDonald posing for a painting depicting the "Spirit of Service" 1888 Blizzard episode.

Repair work goes on in the aftermath of one of Staten Island's worst fires. Charred trees, heaped debris and telephone linemen on the job are starkly outlined against the sky.

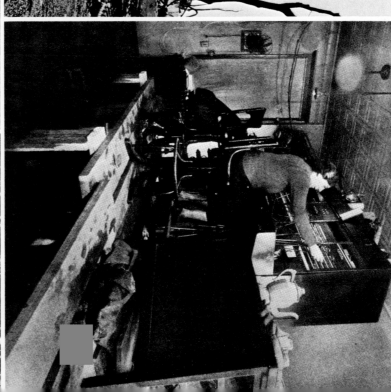

Switchboard at Point Pleasant, West Virginia, was raised on a platform above water 18 inches deep on the second floor. Service continued under these conditions for a week before the water receded. The teapot and dishes on the desk show where makeshift meals were eaten. (1936).

17

manholes, or dealing with a person in difficulty who needs assistance.

Before the advent of electrical communications, older economics textbooks used "communications" as synonymous with modes of transportation — railroads, canals, roads, ships and bridges — and "messages" were confined to either oral reports by weary travelers or to written letters carried from place to place. Even the telegraph (Greek for "farwriting") tried to emulate the copy of a *real* letter. The evolution of every society depends on such means of interaction among its members by facilitating their *physical* movement. Central streets of towns and villages still carry the idea of congregations of people meeting on Main Street, High Street, Market Street, Broad Street and Broadway. The tendency since biblical times for all trades, crafts, dealers and professions to settle into common districts is still with us, diminishing only now under explosions of population and fracturing of old communities. The telephone was the first device to allow the *spirit* of a person, expressed in his own voice, to carry its own message directly without the transportation of his body. This was the quiet social revolution inherent in its character, so little remarked in its origins, yet fundamentally responsible for its phenomenal growth. It was a *liberating* force of the first magnitude. Certainly it is hard to see how the United States population could have grown the way it did from 50 millions in 1876 to 220 millions in 1976, without the enhanced "nervous system" provided by this invention.

"Fear is what is needed in a despotism. Virtue is not at all necessary, and honor would be dangerous". *Montesquieu*

The powerful combination of automobile and telephone created the possibilities for suburban and exurban living, by providing mobility, safety and inter-community access. In fact, the telephone system is a form of "society insurance" and no one knows how many lives are daily saved or injuries prevented by its reliability and speed of access to every kind of service and assistance.

New patterns of commerce, trade, and government have built on the system: finance and travel, decentralized manufacturing plants, regional offices, libraries, retail and wholesale purchasing. "Let Your Fingers Do The Walking", a slogan of the indispensable Yellow Pages classified advertising, encapsulated a profound social shift in the way shopping had been done for countless generations. To many people, that thick compendium of specialized help or services is their most-used reference work, and listings like *AAAAAA Atomic Television Repair Shop* (named to be at the head of its alphabetized columns) show how canny proprietors respect the instinctive behavior of customers faced with breakdowns of their household equipment.

The rise of international travel has seen another alliance blossom: jet planes for movement, telephones for maintaining contact with home. Overseas calling is the fastest growing sector of telephone usage, doubling every three years. Political campaigns, selling by telephone calls, polling opinion on public questions, and even Christmas card mailing, all depend on the existence of directories furnished without charge to all users. They represent a symbolic map of a community's members. We tend to take their existence for granted, but in Japan, after World War II, easily-remembered telephone numbers were sold at auction, due to the lack of a directory service. France, Britain, Russia and the United States coop-

18

Telephone Linemen, Peoples Republic of China.

Line drawing illustrating emergency value of early telephone booth, used by Chicago police in 1881.

Huge pile of old New York City directories ready for the pulp mill. (1900's). Today, Western Electric technicians use advanced methods to recycle paper for new directories.

Woman using 1927 desk set while thumbing through the Yellow Pages.

Excerpt from the 1976 New York City Yellow Pages.

erated to keep Berlin's telephone system functioning even during the bitter controversies.

We love the telephone *and* hate it at certain moments in our lives, whether awaiting news of safe arrival for a loved one, or repulsing the interruption of a bumptious, fast-talking salesman.

Few inventions which founded great businesses have been able to sustain their importance for a century without decline or collapse. But the key to the telephone's business history may be found in its personal use by an expanding population. The criteria of success applied to any telephone system is how well it responds to the basic human needs for one member of a society to be a part of a larger community, allowing him to talk with his neighbors, family, or friends, associates in business or profession, or people whose help or services he needs. And he wants to do this at will, any time of night or day, to any place in his nation or the world, at prices he can afford and thinks reasonable. It is a challenge fit for scientific genius and noble character, for cool managerial judgment, and the warmest of individual service — each has a place and is found in every nook and cranny of that human and technical system that we call "the phone."

Even increase in social status, one of the foibles of American life, has been affected by this device and its appurtenances. The life story of a Hollywood star has been described in three sentences:

> Early Days — "You can get me on the coin
>   box at the Druggist next door."
>
> First Job — "Call me. I'm in the book."
> Established — "Call my agent. Only he has
>   my unlisted number."

Now we can examine the historical context in which this device became an extension of the senses of human beings who had almost no awareness of what was about to happen to them and their world order.

"Evil communications corrupt good manners."
I Corinthians

"He said, 'Tell the Telephone Company to go fly a kite.'"

Drawing by Booth; © 1976 The New Yorker Magazine, Inc.

22

CHAPTER

2

2

COMMUNICATIONS BEFORE 1876

Imagine that in some reverse science fiction you find yourself displaced backward in time to the United States of the 19th century. What sort of "world" would you see about you, or be aware of from a newspaper of the day? . . . The year is 1876. . . .

In 1876, most of the South was still occupied by Federal troops, eleven years after the Civil War.

TRAVEL: Horses would be everywhere, and horse-stealing a capital crime, since loss of this primary means of transportation could lead to terrible hardships or even death. Forty-six million people were resident in the country, two out of three living in rural areas. They needed about 20 million horses to support their lives both for power and travel. Town and city dwellers moved about on vehicles with less speed than those available to Rome in Caesar's time. For those few who traveled between cities, railroads provided speeds twice that of a fast horse. Railroads were being built at a furious pace. Floods of immigrant labor added two-thousand miles of track each year to the seventy-five thousand miles already built since 1830 when Peter Cooper's Baltimore and Ohio first linked Baltimore to Ellicott Mills, using thirteen miles of track designed for horse cars.

INFORMATION: You would read of General Custer's defeat by Indians at the Little Big Horn and of Colorado's admission to the Union as a state. All daily information came to you in letters, newspapers, books or face-to-face conversation. If any of it concerned matters more than twenty-five miles away, it came to you at least one day old. Before the practical invention of the telegraph (1845), you would be limited to the speeds of *transportation* available for packages and persons if you had to receive or send news of any emergency or unexpected event.

There was no other way, except by military or naval systems which were limited to only the most urgent news.

Thus *time* and *transportation* were treated as synonymous for communication purposes. This identity was — and in many parts of the world remains — deeply ingrained in man. A story told by a young African tribal prince who returned home after schooling in Europe illustrates the attitude. He showed his father, the king, a modern map of their kingdom he had constructed according to our convention of equal *distances* on the ground shown as equal distances on the map. After having pointed out to him on the map, the king commented, "But, my son, you show three finger lengths from the forest to the river, and three finger lengths across the mountains. How can that be?"

"My father, *both* are twenty miles apart."

"But, it takes us only two days to the river, and six days to cross the mountains."

"True, but the European maps say nothing about how long it takes, only how far apart places are."

"Then European maps are absurd. What good are they, to mislead people that way? *Our* old maps are better because they show how long it takes us to make a journey, and *that's* what a traveler wants to know. We will not use such foolishness. I hope you learned better things than this!" Before we smile at the old chief, think how many times your questions about travel have been answered in hours rather than miles. All of us have a far better developed sense of *time* than of *distance.* Military and naval tactics are always translated into matters of

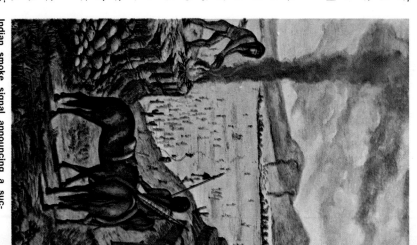

Indian smoke signal announcing a successful war party.

1976 Transaction® Telephone's Internal Wiring. The highest state of telephony. Transaction uses solid state circuitry, much of it developed by Bell Telephone Laboratories. Transaction telephones are used for direct computer linkages and displaying information received.
®Trademark of AT&T Co.

time, even though commanders have superb maps to aid their decisions. "Git there fustest with the mostest" was General Forrest's prescription for military success, and it is still valid for many conflict situations of modern life.

Until 1876, the severe limitations of time existed as an unconquerable frustration. Any idea or invention seeking to reduce the time needed to transmit information received a hopeful, friendly audience and usually enjoyed trial demonstrations. Speed records have been recorded since antiquity and are still reported as serious news. Today, eager newcomers continue to set up targets for new assaults on our old frustrations, from foot racing to space rockets, hoping to "shorten" distances and accelerate the flow of intelligence.

The National Baseball League was founded, Johns Hopkins University opened, and Colorado became a State in 1876.

In order to acquire a "feel" for the speeds available to human beings before electrical communications, let us examine some of the records of human and technical achievement. Only then

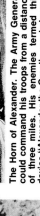

The Horn of Alexander. The Army General could command his troops from a distance of three miles. His enemies termed this device "Alexander the Great's magic horn."

The runner Pheidippides.

can one appreciate the strange devices and costly schemes as well as the riotous welcome given authentic inventions of rapid communication.

A legendary feat is that of Pheidippides, the best runner of his time, who carried news of the Greek victory over a Persian invading army at Marathon, in 490 B.C. After covering the 22 miles in something over three hours, he gasped out the news, then fell dead of exertion. It is hard to see how one could establish a commercial service on these lines — recruiting would be difficult — but runners have always been used in military affairs, and still are. The current record for a 30-mile run is a bit under four hours, and the longest distance ever run in one day is 133 miles. Great improvements of these speeds are unlikely. The best known performance for a large body of men, marching with equipment and under discipline, is 42 miles in 26 hours. That occurred in 1809. The effort was necessary for the Light Brigade to relieve the Duke of Wellington after the bloody battle of Talavera in Spain against Napoleon's armies.
HORSES: Human limitations made the horse a welcome ad-

A King receives a messenger in his war tent. From a 14th century painting.

Napoleon crossing the Alps. From a painting by Jacques-Louis David. "Napoleon," his contemporary, the famous Madame de Staël said, "was an able chess player and the human race was the opponent to whom he proposed to give checkmate."

junct to man's needs. Centuries of improvements in breeding, training, harnesses and wheeled vehicles achieved the following records of performance which still stand today. (Ordinary, everyday experience was, of course, far below these.) *Champion Grabbet*, carrying 245 pounds, covered 300 miles in fifty-two and a half hours. But the news of the "shot heard 'round the world" at the Battle of Lexington took four days to reach New York and eleven more to carry the message to Charleston, South Carolina.

The stagecoach is rich in literature and adventure. Few costume films or stories dare exclude it. The best speed ever done with coach-and-four was a round trip between London and Brighton, 108 miles, using eight teams and fourteen changes, taking just under eight hours for an average speed of 14 miles an hour. The best coaching time was 21 miles per hour. The owner of an average cob would consider himself sorely tried to cover 25 miles in one day.

Small margins of excellence could produce great results. The

Napoleonic lieutenant, Baron de Marbot, writes admiringly of his British foes, the only nation which brought thoroughbred hunters to battles for carrying messages. Marbot said that his fellow soldiers were so impressed with the speed and elegance of these dashing couriers that they would not shoot at them for fear of hitting "those splendid beasts." They often applauded a great jump since no French horse could ever overtake them! As we shall see below, the French used other mechanical means to offset the advantage, even though the Emperor Napoleon always established relays of officer riders to keep him in touch with Paris no matter where his ambition led him — up to and from Moscow.

Every nineteenth century cavalry officer was assumed to be a message carrier. A close look at their uniforms will show a small leather pouch with quick-acting clasp, worn on a back strap, which was always to be kept empty, ready to be filled with handwritten orders from commanders and adjutants.

Paul Revere's ride, learned in verse by generations of schoolchildren, showed one of the first attempts at colonial military "broadcasting." From a communications viewpoint, Revere was the final link in a message chain involving telescopes and coded lanterns in a church tower, retailing his alarms to people who had to make life-and-death choices. (Today's revolutionary practice calls for seizing a country's central broadcasting station just before arresting its prime minister, since reception of the *message* of the act is more important than the act itself.)

If George Washington had been able to telephone King George III and talk things over, would there have been an American Revolution? *College History test.*

The early postal systems relied on horsepower. It was the foundation of the national same-charge "Penny Post" (using adhesive stamps for the first time) established in England in 1840 by Rowland Hill, and later imported by America. A clerk in the British Post Office, the distinguished novelist, Anthony Trollope, suggested placing the "pillar box," or American "mail box," on street corners as a way to speed up collection and to give twenty-four-hour access to the public. The postal services of the world have developed, encouraged, and often subsidized improvements in transportation to assist rapid delivery of written information. Theodore Vail, first General Manager of the Bell Telephone Company (see Chapter VII) was superintendent of railway mail operations for the United States, where he invented the method of sorting letters on moving trains just before he transferred his talents to electrical communications.

Thus, horses, and the masses who used and served them, carried out the communication function of societies for thousands of years. In this respect, our great-grandfathers were far closer to medieval men than to us. Today, we see this once indispensable animal mostly in sport and spectacle.

ROADS AND BRIDGES: The history of roads parallels the development of central cities. By 400 B.C., all Persian provinces were connected by roads to the capital, Susa. One road was 1,500 miles long. Roman roads were essential to Roman government. When strong central control was lost after the fall of Rome, roads were neglected.

Until the nineteenth century, no adequate road network was available in most nations. Postal systems were operated by private companies, the most durable being Thurn and Taxis, (from whom our word "taxi" developed) an Italian family knighted by the Holy Roman Emperor in 1450 and, after Germanicizing their name, given the only feudal fiefdom without land. The position Imperial Postmaster General was made a hereditary title and the family established and carried out postal services all over Europe until finally bought out by Prussia in 1867. Their post houses and routes set the foundation of subsequent road networks.

In the early nineteenth century, new methods of making roads were employed by Macadam and Telford in Britain, using compacted crushed stone which became firmer as traffic increased. This method was copied all over the world and its fundamental theories are still used today by civil engineers. Roads and railroads required spanning of natural barriers, and bridge design entered its golden age. All forms — arch, stone, iron, truss, suspension, cantilever — advanced rapidly. Extraordinary heights and spans were successfully achieved in many parts of the world.

The Pony Express, one of the most colorful communications services, was considered ideal for the American West in

The news reaches small town America before the advent of the telephone.

Brooklyn Bridge under construction (ca. 1877).

Lithograph of 18th century mail carrier.

Paul Revere's ride warning the Patriots that the British were coming, April 18, 1775.

1860. Even at charges of $5 per half-ounce, the 11-day service between St. Joseph, Missouri and San Francisco went bankrupt in a year. But it did succeed in stimulating the national belief in the value of fast messages and the urgent need for better transportation in developing territories.

Canals probably lowered freight charges faster and further than any other transportation innovation in world history. They allowed horses to pull thousands of times their weight in nearly frictionless, still water. Every major country engaged in orgies of canal promotion and building. Railroads gradually displaced them. Recently, they have been revived as an extremely low-cost method of transport, especially for large ships and barges. Some historians believe the early, superior development of roads, bridges and canals in Britain guaranteed for many decades its preeminence as leader of the Industrial Revolution.

SHIPS: Sailing vessels have been known since prehistory. Their beauty, efficient use of natural energy, and danger have pro-

Pony Express Rider.

duced a romantic aura that still lingers and appeals. They continually served as carriers, explorers and weapons, and were prime communications links until transoceanic electrical methods and aircraft consigned their message-carrying to slow, surface mail.

Until the age of steam, ships made little improvement in the speeds achieved by Columbus for the Atlantic crossing. In 1854, the record for one day's run under sail was set when *Champion of the Seas* covered 535 miles. The highest speed for sail is 25 miles per hour, set by *Lancing* on the Australian run in 1890. But the hazards lurking in the vagaries of wind and weather are underlined in the *slowest* voyage on record, made by *Red Rock,* taking 112 days for 950 miles in the Coral Sea. She was so late that the insurance was paid. Her average speed was a half mile per hour.

Even aided by steam and modern engineering, transatlantic voyages were lengthy. The first powered crossing in 1827 took 22 days. In 1952, the liner *United States* did it in three-and-a-half

East River waterfront, New York, 1876.

"The 19th century invented the idea of inventions." Anon.

PIGEONS: The "frictionless" air, and apparent ease with which birds covered vast distances swiftly, exercised man's imagination since Icarus test-piloted artificial wings (designed by his father, Daedalus) with fatal consequences. The sea, into which he fell acquired the name Icarian as small compensation for his daring. Yet others continued this dangerous assault on nature for centuries. The early Greeks developed a hybrid form of communication based on vicarious transportation and the peculiar ability of a bird species, carrier pigeons, which can navigate back to their home base by methods still not understood. Carrier pigeons announced victories in the Olympic Games (776 B.C.-393 A.D.).

With messages carried in tiny tubes attached to their legs, pigeons have played crucial roles in many events. In 1815, bankers made a killing on the stock exchange using the earliest news of the Battle of Waterloo brought by homing pigeons to London. The Duke of Wellington was a pigeon fancier, and one of his birds still holds the long distance record of 7,000 miles in 55 days, from West Africa to England, where it fell dead, in the tradition of great communications feats. Late into the nineteenth century, Reuter's News Agency used pigeons to

days, top speed of 48 miles per hour. At the time of the invention of the telephone, sailing vessels needed from 20 to 36 days, and steamships about 17 days, to make the crossing. The best performance on the mail run in 1895 was 157 hours. Again we see that certain, inexorable limits were reached after enormous and costly efforts to make even small improvements. Further leaps forward would require radically new forms, both for passengers and messages. This is a familiar theme in the history of invention, and the term "breakthrough" implies a complete penetration of old, stubborn obstacles which can only be surmounted by a true innovation — a *new* way — rather than increased applications of brute force, or mere persistence of the old.

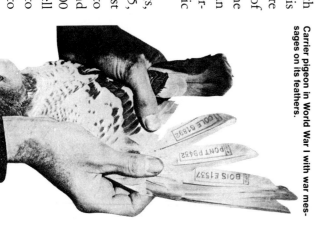

Carrier pigeon in World War I with war messages on its feathers.

fill out its network of telegraph bulletins, and World War I battalions on the Western Front sent messages of desperation from their besieged positions. The longest pigeon flight in twenty-four hours is 803 miles, set in 1941 at San Antonio. These birds probably represent the best that pure transportation, unaided by applied science, can accomplish as communications methods. However, they can only return home, and the required training and transportation to specific points of message origin make their use for a widespread public service awkward and limited. Yet the U.S. Army Signal Corps disbanded its pigeon corps only a few years ago. Twenty-seven centuries of service is a good run for any medium.

VISUAL METHODS: It became apparent toward the end of the eighteenth century that communications *had* to be set free from the shackles of primitive transportation. The burgeoning economic demands of industrialization and increasing nationalist wars demanded exact information speedily transmitted. Visual methods were an attractive solution. Greeks and Romans used signal fires and torches since antiquity. Indian smoke signals and African tom-toms spiced accounts of adventurous travelers. The invention of the telescope reawakened interest in those methods. The great English physicist, Robert Hooke (1635-1703), a contemporary of Sir Isaac Newton, delivered a comprehensive, detailed plan for visual telegraphy to the Royal Society in 1684. But this method was never tried in practice. The use of *light* to overcome the frustrations of time comes from its speed which, to most people, is nearly infinite. Light laughs at distance. From the outer recesses of the universe to a wink across a room, we think of it as instantaneous — and, except to quantum physicists, nothing *moves* to send the message. As happens often in the history of technology, Hooke's idea lay dormant for a hundred years, until the needs of war made necessary what peace found impractical.

The faint blue quasar, QSO OQ172, is the remotest, visible object from Earth, 91,700,000,000,000,000,000,000 miles away.

In 1793, the uproar of the French Revolution put the entire nation under attack. A brilliant engineer, Claude Chappe, resurrecting Hooke's idea, saw that a system of rapid, internal communications could help offset the combined, but uncoordinated, armies of Britain, Holland, Prussia, Austria and Spain. He developed a semaphore arrangement. Wooden arms were placed in different positions on top of towers representing letters of the alphabet. Trained men turned cranks housed in a room below the tower and used telescopes to read messages sent them from adjacent towers. (The system's configuration was remarkably similar to microwave radio relay towers which march across today's landscape at spacings based on the line-of-sight between them.) M. Chappe's system was so successful, in speed and accuracy, that France was covered by 556 semaphore stations stretching nearly 5,000 kilometers until electrical telegraphy superseded it in 1852. The expense was so great that financial controversy was constant. Finally, a public lottery produced the required funds.

Britain soon followed Chappe's system, constructing a semaphore network to administer Admiralty affairs between naval bases and London. The term "Telegraph Hill," familiar in many English and American coastal towns, dates from these times and uses. (Boston and Martha's Vineyard were the points served first in the United States, handling mostly shipping news.) When properly manned, the systems were swift. One

Claude Chappe's Semaphore system.

Chappe's Optical Telegraph. Arrangements of the vertical and horizontal beams created the message which was viewed by telescope at the distant end. Device consists of two arms operated by chain below.

French Army using Chappe's military Optical Telegraph.

South American wood-slab signal device, used in dense jungles along the Amazon, is a xylophone type of apparatus and can transmit sounds of different pitches.

Top: The cylinder system of Aeneas Tacitus, first used about 330 B.C., was fairly effective in clear weather for transmitting messages over a distance of five or six miles. Both sender and receiver had identical equipment. On the first smoke signal both allowed water to run from the cylinders, thus lowering the height of the horizontally lined message gauge affixed to a wooden float on the water's surface. When the sender's gauge had reached the desired line, he signalled the receiver who closed his own apparatus. The line related to a message list previously agreed upon.

Whispering Rod. Few houses in Colonial days had more than one room for the reception of visitors. The young people resorted to this ingenious method of communication.

33

test between London and Plymouth recorded 500 miles covered in three minutes. Today, the use of the semaphore is limited to those movable arms of railway signals, and signalmen on ships, who use their own arms, equipped with flags, to spell out letters. The modern visual signal is a searchlight mounted with shutters (like a venetian blind) called a "blinker" which allows naval technicians to send the dots-and-dashes of the Morse Code in flashes of light to other vessels. Semaphore systems exhausted their potential in a few decades. They were expensive to construct, operators needed training in coding ordinary language, and weather conditions made them vulnerable to failure. Yet their successful *demonstration* of the *value* of rapid communication set the stage for *electrical* telegraphs as the social progeny of the visual.

THE TELEGRAPH: While human ingenuity battered in-

Hans Christian Oerstedt (1777-1851). In addition to his work on magnetism and electricity, he was the first scientist to isolate aluminum.

finity with bare fists — trying to use the swiftness of light to carry messages — a simple, accidental experiment in 1820 at Copenhagen dramatically changed history. At an evening lecture, Hans Christian Oersted noticed that when he connected a battery to wires looping around his desk, the needle of a nearby compass turned, and when disconnected, the needle returned to normal. This happened anywhere along the entire length of the wire, and without the compass touching it. (It can be done by a child, and needs only a flashlight battery, a short length of wire, and a toy compass.) Oersted had discovered what we know as the electromagnetic field — the foundation for all subsequent electrical communications, motors and dynamos. Those alert for new communications methods appreciated the possibilities of sending signals. Theoretically, the length of the wire used to loop between two points could be limitless.

Connecting and disconnecting a battery in one town could cause a compass needle in another town to flip between "connect" and "disconnect." Thus, the electrical telegraph found its principle.

Previous methods which tried to use electricity were somewhat bizarre, though given real trials. Until Oersted, the only readily available form of electricity was "static" electricity — a comb run through dry hair causing it to fluff and follow the comb; a shock suffered on touching a doorknob after walking briskly across a carpet; a flash of lightning — these are all forms of static electricity, which was thought to move extremely fast when "discharged," i.e., when the shock or spark was produced. One religious experimenter, the Abbé Nollet (1700-1770), had sufficient power to mount a test. He arranged 200 Carthusian monks in a mile-long circle. Each monk held two wires. Then, the Abbé passed a shock to the 2 monks at each

end. All 200 monks jumped simultaneously. The good Abbé showed the speed to be practically instantaneous. A Spanish nobleman, Don Salva of Barcelona, used Leyden jars (which "stored" static electricity) to send messages by shocking human "receivers" at the end of a wire line. The Spanish Royal Family used this system (over 28 miles) for sending private messages, though the attitude of recruits to this service is not recorded.

Bell Telephone Laboratories is at work on a system to connect a 3,000 mile telephone call in under two seconds.

Following Oersted's discovery, many European inventors joined in the chase. Baron Schilling in Russia and Gauss in Germany made operable devices. But William Cooke, a young East India Company soldier, invalided back to England, saw Schilling's apparatus, and constructed several new forms, one intended for the new Liverpool-Manchester Railway. Technical difficulties caused him to form an alliance with Charles

2

Evolution of the telegraph key.

Wheatstone, professor of Natural Philosophy at Kings College. In 1837, they received their patent for a five-needle telegraph and installed a working line on the Great Western Railway. Other railroads followed immediately. As in much of communications history, the public's attention was seized by a spectacular incident. A murderer was caught escaping on a train. His description and carriage seat number were sent ahead by the new telegraph. Thus message speed was seen to exceed the fastest known form of transportation. The telegraph became the "talk" of the country. Newspapers, eager to advertise their speeded access to events, included "Telegraph" in their titles. For their achievement, Cooke and Wheatstone were knighted by Queen Victoria.

The American, Samuel Finley Breeze Morse (1791-1872) became interested in electromagnets shown him by a fellow passenger during a return voyage from Europe in 1832. True to the tradition of men from one field making inventions in

A re-enactment of the sending of the first telegram by Morse, May 24, 1844. The words, "What hath God wrought?" are from *Numbers, XXIII* and were suggested by the daughter of the Commissioner of Patents.

another, Morse was a distinguished painter of historical subjects, and professor of the Literature of Arts and Design at New York University. His idea used an electromagnet holding a pen to mark a moving strip of paper with "dots" and "dashes" in response to a key (or switch) manipulated by an operator at a distant point. Morse arranged his code to minimize time by assigning simple combinations to most frequently used letters. His practical orientation is shown by how he determined frequency: Morse simply counted the number of letters found in each box of a printer's type case. Thus, a permanent "written" record of the message was produced. In 1844, a telegraph line between Washington and Baltimore carried the first message "What hath God wrought?" In the next twenty years, infant telegraph companies blossomed everywhere. Hiram Sibley consolidated many of them into the Western Union Telegraph Company in 1865. Expansion rapidly followed and in 1866 Western Union owned 2,250 offices and had 100,000 miles of lines. One great impetus was the development of a

The arrival of the Atlantic Cable in Newfoundland.

telegraphic news service, led by the Associated Press. Interest in acquiring a telegraph network was worldwide. Soon the need to bridge the oceans was obvious. After a decade of heroic efforts and heartbreaking failures, the largest steamship in the world, *Great Eastern*, successfully completed the transatlantic cable linking America to Europe in 1866. Lord Kelvin, the greatest scientist of the time, was an outstanding technical contributor to the entire venture. He was destined to play an important role in the later saga of Alexander Graham Bell. But his early involvement with electrical communications in their telegraphic form established the conditions of his interest and predisposed him to an alertness for any new breakthrough.

A fantastic collection of talents, geniuses, promoters, charlatans, entrepreneurs, statesmen and visionaries all contributed to this first fevered rush into the telecommunications age. Each

played an important role in dramatizing to a stirring world the opportunities for economic and social progress implicit in crossing the threshold into our own Age.

"Attention, universe! By Kingdoms, right wheel!" *Part of a message sent by Morse in an early (1837) telegraph demonstration.*

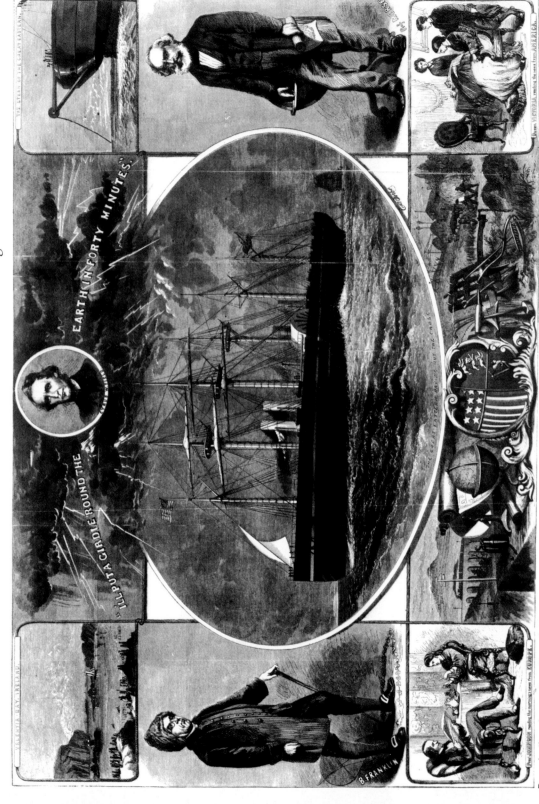

Reproduction of pages from Harper's Weekly, Aug. 12, 1865 in connection with the laying of the first Transatlantic Telegraph Cable — which was placed in operation the following year.

38

CHAPTER

3

THE LONELY ADVENTURE OF PERSONAL INVENTION: BELL'S EARLY YEARS

"No great discovery was ever made without a bold guess."
Isaac Newton

Our word "invent" comes from the Latin root for "come upon" or "discover." Yet, our idea of "inventor" or "invention" usually means a deliberate, often fanatical, pursuit of solutions to technical problems. A problem, by its nature, is a mismatch between what we have and what we want. It creates a psychological state akin to frustration until the "problem" is solved — or abandoned. Such conflict, if only in the mind of the inventor, sets up the essential condition of drama. Sagas of individual inventors and inventions are rich in the structural elements of good dramas — conflict, development and resolution. The inventors and the invention of the telephone are not exceptions, and their story bristles with more coincidences, perversities, humor, legal battles, pathos, anxieties and triumphs than most writers of fiction would allow.

Inventors possess two other aspects which characterize them as a peculiar class of human beings: highly developed streaks of exhibitionism and compulsion for periods of solitary contemplation. They carry the normal rhythms of life — involvement and withdrawal — to wild extremes, sometimes to the point of manic-depressive pathology. (Our inventors here happily stopped short of this disaster.) One final observation suggested by an overview of inventions of the eighteenth and nineteenth centuries is how seldom genuine breakthroughs were made by the "professionals" or experts in a particular area. Most seminal inventors appear to have come to their field of success after accomplishments in other disciplines or vocations. Their naive, almost innocent, approaches to longstanding problems; their unpretentious willingness to ask fundamental questions; their

ability to admit ignorance of things all professionals "knew" — these qualities allowed them to explore avenues of possibility considered fruitless by eminent persons. Alexander Graham Bell was an outstanding example of this phenomenon of the "marginal man" — one who brings a specialized kit of personal tools developed in one field to the frontier challenges of another.

CHILDHOOD: Alexander Bell — the "Graham" came later — was born in Edinburgh, Scotland, on March 3, 1847. His grandfather, who played a large role in Bell's development, was a cobbler, like generations of his forebears. But there lurked in him a flair that shoemaking in St. Andrews could not use, nor quench. We find his occupation listed on the marriage register as "comedian." He played all sorts of minor parts, often using Scottish dialect. He kept a tavern, and ended his stage career as a prompter. Here he trained himself in both resonant speaking and well-pronounced English. (This last is no small accomplishment, especially when one undertakes, as this Bell did, to teach English to Englishmen.)

To acquire a respectable Scottish wife, he had to abandon the disreputable theatre. But after his marriage he read Shakespeare's plays from lecture platforms and taught clients "methods to correct defective utterance." Thus, the seeds of a genetic heritage toward preoccupation with human speech were sown, affecting the lives of both his son and grandson. A scandalous divorce ruined him financially and caused him to set

out for London in 1833 to begin a new life. He took with him his fourteen-year-old son, Alexander Melville Bell, the inventor's father. Bell's grandfather brought out two books, *The Practical Elocutionist and Stammering, and Other Impediments to Speech.*

In 1838, he sent Melville to Newfoundland to regain his failing health. He recovered and this furnished the precedent for his own son in later years. Melville built a reputation there in speech, both theatrical and therapeutic, which laid the foundation for his later profession when he returned to London in 1842. He soon began his profound and novel investigations of speech organs which continued until his death. Visiting Edinburgh, he met Eliza Grace Symonds, who was a painter, daughter of a naval family — and deaf. He married her there in 1844 and set up as a "Professor of Elocution." On March 3, 1847, their second son was born, christened simply "Alexander." (The "Graham" was added at the age of eleven when he appropriated it from a friend of the family, a Cuban planter named Alexander Graham.) He had a happy childhood, filled with both the urban and rural recreations of Scotland. Yet

he showed no academic distinction at all. His elder brother took the prizes. At fourteen, young Alexander left school and went to live with his seventy-year-old grandfather in London. (Considering the inconvenience and difficulties of nineteenth century travel, one is struck by the ease with which Bell took to travel all through his long life. He learned the art early, and the use of the telephone as a substitute was never lost on one accustomed to purposeful wandering.) The year he spent in London under his grandfather's tutelage shaped his life and made him chafe at being treated as a boy on his return to Edinburgh. Characteristically, he applied for a job as teacher at a boys' school in Elgin, (neglecting to mention his age of 16) and became a tutor in music and elocution. Aware of total deficiency in Greek and Latin, he studied those for a year at the University of Edinburgh, then promptly returned to Elgin as a top-hatted resident master, aged 17. On Sundays, he eagerly escaped to the solitude of a nearby ruined abbey and established that alternation of action and seclusion which formed the rhythm of his life. His independent research in sound began at Elgin, and in 1865 Alexander Graham Bell discovered vowel

Early 19th century view of Edinburgh, Scotland.

Alexander Graham Bell's birthplace, Edinburgh, Scotland.

Eliza Grace Bell

Alexander Melville Bell (1819-1905). Inventor of Visible Speech symbols.

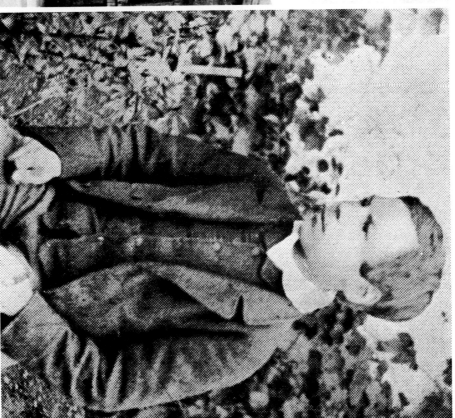

Alexander Graham Bell, aged 11.

43

formation to be rooted in the resonance cavities of the mouth.

Melville moved to London on the death of his father. While in Edinburgh, he had developed — and acquired some fame from — a system of writing down symbols for speech sounds. One trained in Melville Bell's "Visible Speech" could shape his voice cavities to reproduce the original sounds with astounding precision. Young Alexander and his brother became expert demonstrators of the method performed during the father's public lectures. At a tender age, Alexander found himself at ease on the platform — an ability which would remain with him throughout his life.

One effect of Bell's Visible Speech was the inspiration it gave to George Bernard Shaw's *Pygmalion* and in the musical version of it, *My Fair Lady*. Professor Higgins is modeled on Melville. Teaching a Cockney flower girl to form her speech like a duchess is the heart of the satire. The idea of Scotsmen correcting and tutoring the elocution of Englishmen implies

Alexander Graham Bell, aged 20 (1867).

its own theatrical elements — and dramatic elements attend the careers of all the Bells, especially Alexander.

At this time, science, in all its branches, was the stuff of conversation in London society. Controversies and theories abounded; popular lectures and demonstrations were the fashion. No age could have furnished greater stimulus to the energetic and curious minds of people like the Bells. While biology, polarized by Darwin, held center stage, electricity was in the air. Atlantic cable, telegraphs, applications to acoustics, and great men like Wheatstone and Kelvin fired the average man's imagination. One incident illustrates the charming innocence of this period of popular science. Bell's father told him of the great Helmholtz's paper (in German) on the use of electrical tuning forks to produce a vowel sound. Bell's inability to read German, and the ambiguity of the illustrations, led him to believe that Helmholtz had sent the sounds by telegraph. Unable to duplicate the imagined experiment, Bell did not know his error until 1870, when he read the paper in French. His later comment is a beautiful example of how he was constantly led into right paths by multiple ignorance: "I thought Helmholtz had done it and that my failure was due only to my ignorance of electricity. It was a very valuable blunder. It gave me confidence. If I had been able to read German, I might never have begun my experiments in electricity."

Bell's father became a famous man. He was appointed professor of Elocution at the University of London and was elected to membership in the Philological Society. Visible Speech was a recognized scientific achievement, *Bell's Standard Elocutionist* was a best seller. His father's fame led Alexander to an acquaintance with the intellectual life of the capital. But his youngest brother died of tuberculosis, an especially bitter tragedy for Melville, and Alexander left Scotland for a teaching post at Bath, moving closer to his parents. He soon joined them in London. With characteristic energy, he threw himself

into the academic and professional uproar that swirled about his father. He studied anatomy and physiology at University College, began successful sessions with a deaf child who learned to speak for the first time using Visible Speech, read long hours at the British Museum, and taught the manifold arts of elocution both in public lectures and to private clients. Melville's fame had spread by now to the United States. Boston's Lowell Institute invited him to conduct a series of lectures. Alexander shouldered the entire workload. He was twenty-one.

On Melville's return to London after a great triumph in America, Alexander's older brother contracted tuberculosis and died suddenly in 1870, at Edinburgh. Nearly demoralized with grief at the loss of two sons, Melville feared that Alec, weary and pale from overwork, would die too. A London physician confirmed the distraught parent's fears. With no thought to the professional life and stature for which he had

Rex Harrison playing Doctor Henry Higgins in *My Fair Lady*. Notice Melville Bell's Visible Speech symbols.

Hermann Ludwig Ferdinand von Helmholtz (1821-1894). Among his other accomplishments, he invented the ophthalmoscope.

labored so hard, Melville immediately decided to remove Alexander from the dangers of the British winters. His youthful experience in Newfoundland, where his own health was restored, made it the first choice. The now diminished family intended a two-year trial in the New World. But they never returned.

CANADA: After a fourteen-day Atlantic crossing, the family took a steamer from Quebec for Ontario. In a few days — the habit of swift decision again asserting itself — Melville bought a little farmhouse with an orchard and birch grove placed prettily on the Grand River, four miles from the town of Brantford, old Mohawk Indian country. In the clear air, Alec's health miraculously improved. In April, 1871, Alexander substituted for his father in a series of lectures which had been contracted for by Boston's School for the Deaf. He blossomed in this intellectual capital of the New World. Within months he conducted the sessions, repeated them in Northhampton, Massachusetts, taught for some weeks in Hartford, Connect-

icut, and took pupils in Newton Lower Falls. He addressed a National Conference of leaders in deaf education at Flint, Michigan. The title of his address was "Speech."

Over 25 million immigrants came to America between 1870 and 1914.

Activity on this scale in our time of rapid travel and communication would be remarkable. But when one considers the obstacles to such effort in the 1870s, it is amazing — especially for a person recently told he had six months to live. Returning to Ontario for the winter, Bell resumed his abandoned experiments in Helmholtz's work. Sympathetic vibration — in its theoretical and empirical aspects — dominated his mind during this period of withdrawal and contemplation. Those long sessions at a piano, singing pure tones and listening for whispers of resonance with the strings, were unconsciously laying the foundation and sharpening his faculties for the great work of his life. That he acquired a local reputation of "being peculiar" seems a small, if inevitable, price to pay.

3

BOSTON: While Bell was not an entrepreneur in our ordinary sense of the word, the speed and lack of tentativeness with which he organized his efforts on an often precarious commercial basis is astonishing. In someone less gifted or energetic, it would have been rash. So, in October 1872, we find Bell, at twenty-five, setting up a "School of Vocal Physiology" on West Newton Street in Boston. His announcement is characteristic and carries phrasing similar to his grandfather's original advertisement when he did the same years before in Scotland: "For the correction of stammering and other defects of utterance and for practical instruction in visible speech, conducted by Alexander Graham Bell, member of the Philological Society of London."

As a sideline, he began and edited a manuscript periodical called the *Visible Speech Pioneer.* From here, Bell's story becomes so rich in coincidences that a novelist would not dare employ

Boston in 1870.

them. As Mark Twain said, "Of course, truth is stranger than fiction; fiction has to make sense." That a pioneer teacher of the deaf — where lack of speech is the human tragedy he grapples with — became the inventor of a device which is based totally on human speech is remarkable enough. But the fact is that deafness played an overwhelming part in the events of his life. His own hearing was far beyond normal in sensitivity and range. His mother was deaf, as was his future wife. The two most important backers for his work first met Bell while he was involved with education of those suffering deafness.

SANDERS AND HUBBARD: Thomas Sanders, leather merchant of Haverhill, Massachusetts, had a son, George, who had been born deaf. Gardiner Greene Hubbard was an eminent Boston lawyer blessed with a progressive, promoting mind, whose energy was similar to Bell's. He practiced before the

(Text continues on page 49)

The Telephone Pioneers of America was founded in 1911 by veteran telephone employees. Pioneers are an honor society of men and women, both active and retired, who have given lengthy years of service to the telephone industry in the United States and Canada. Alexander Graham Bell was placed on the membership roll as Pioneer No. 1. The three basic Pioneer aims are: Fellowship, Loyalty, and Service.

Organized under the banner of "United to Serve Others," volunteers seek ways of meeting the special needs of the communities in which they live. Pioneers and their younger associates tutor potential dropouts, repair "talking book" record players for the blind, transcribe many thousands of textbook pages into braille, teach skills to the retarded, make mechanical devices to aid motion and speech handicapped, and screen preschool children for evidences of sight or hearing handicaps. They also entertain at veterans' hospitals, wrap bandages for the Red Cross, and serve as nurses' aides, performing a multitude of useful services to benefit others. In 1976, 195,000 Pioneer members, life members, younger telephone industry employees and family members of telephone people, participated in 1,400 community service projects. There are nearly 500,000 Telephone Pioneers in North America, making it the largest organization of its kind in the world.

Over 100 years ago, Alexander Graham Bell and his family started the philanthropic traditions of aiding the needy — the deaf, the blind and the infirm. Today, Pioneers are the dedicated heirs to this splendid tradition. Telephone Pioneers answer the calls of their neighbors when needed just as Thomas Watson raced from his workshop to Bell's when the great inventor said, in the first recorded telephone message: "Mr. Watson, come here, I want you!"

Pioneers spend countless hours of volunteer time repairing electronic instruments used by the handicapped. Clockwise: record player; tape recorder; tape recorder internal circuit; tape cassette machines.

THE TELEPHONE PIONEERS: A Photographic Essay

Left above: Traffic Light Trainer used in physically handicapped readiness class.

Left: Advanced ELCODE teaching device that contains pre-programmed tapes for unsupervised learning.

Right above: Rear view showing wiring of advanced ELCODE.

Above: Electric Speller — upper and lower case letters plus objects spin to stop when properly aligned.

Electronic Teaching Devices

Right: Pioneers Walter Zimmerman and C. F. Boettcher with their inventions: talking dolls, electric speller and ELectrical COmmunication DEvices (ELCODE) for use by speechless and physically handicapped people. Hundreds of "talking" dogs, bears, rabbits and other animals, as well as dolls, have been made by Pioneer volunteers and distributed to speech therapists across the country. A wireless radio transmitting and receiving system is installed in each toy permitting a speech therapist to communicate with a child while remaining out-of-sight.

Below: ELCODE teaching device in advanced physically handicapped class. Red lights alongside written questions and answers light sequentially. The handicapped child, limited to head motions only, can operate stop-start switch incorporated in head brace with simple turn of head from left to right. The ELCODE adaptations are a major breakthrough in teaching physically handicapped children and adults.

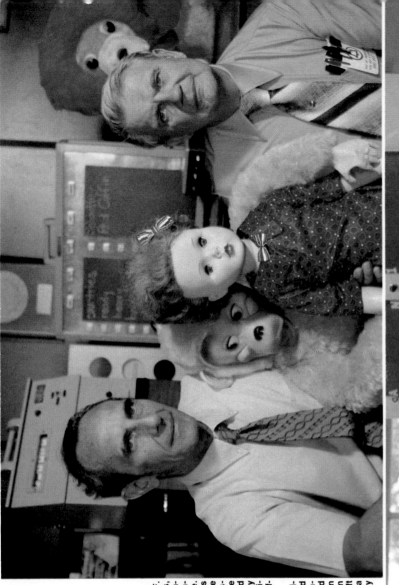

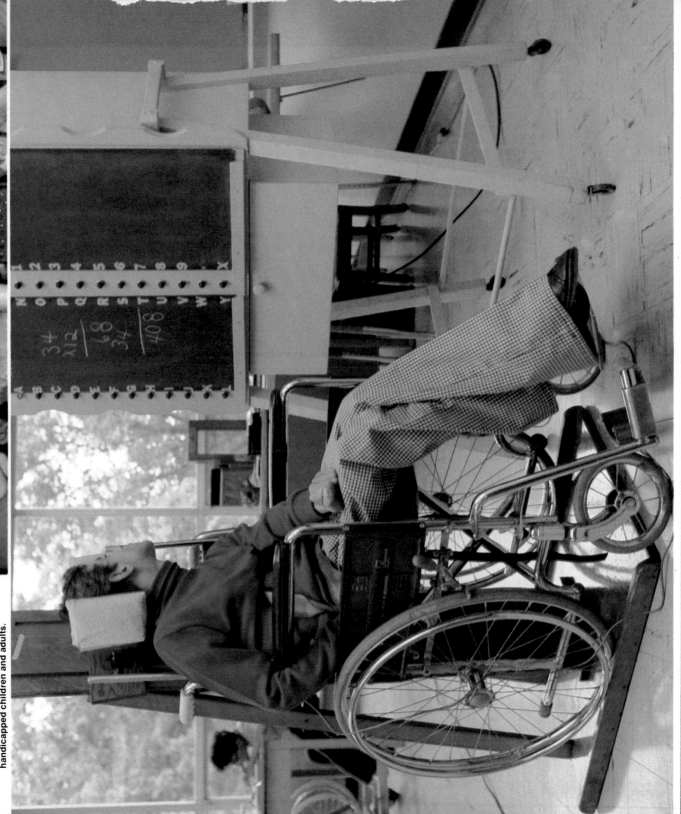

Below: Pioneers teaching handicapped children to work a zipper. Bottom: Retarded children working with Touch book.

Top: Three-dimensional Braille book using raised illustrations to encourage reading by young, visually handicapped children. The printed text is inter-leaved for the assistance of a sighted parent or teacher. Objects are affixed by hand, glued or sewn. Hundreds of these books are distributed to schools and institutions for blind children.

Above: Child working with Braille book.

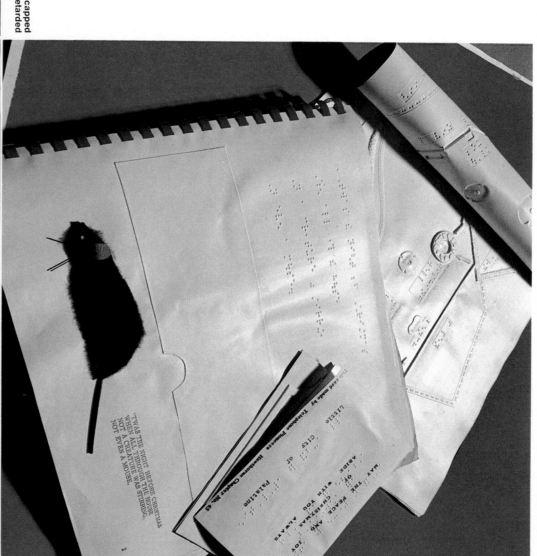

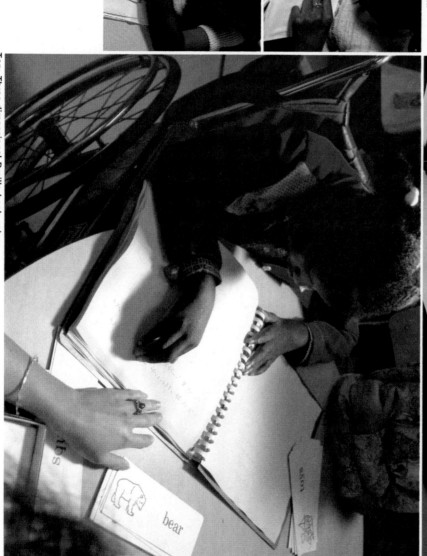

Left above: Blind children at a school for the deaf and blind playing catch with the Audio Ball.

Right above: St. Lawrence Sonadisc — an audio hockey puck for blind players, developed by Canadian Pioneers. May be used on ice or a gymnasium floor. The puck emits a continuous series of high and low tones.

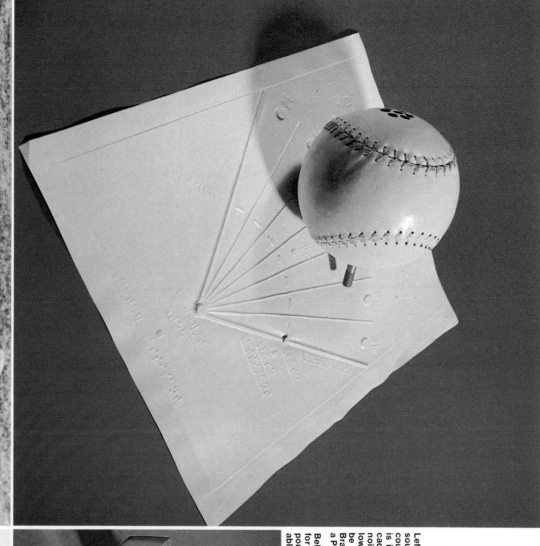

Left: Audio Ball — Pioneers developed this sound-equipped ball so that blind children could play baseball. A plug-in sound module is inserted into the ball powered by nickel cadmium batteries. A pulsating beeping noise is emitted and a blind person can follow the path of the ball. It is strong enough to be hit with a bat and continue beeping. The Braille chart under it describes the layout of a Pioneer Baseball game.

Below: "Cricket" Audio Directional Device for aiding the blind. It weighs less than a pound and was developed originally to enable blind people to avoid obstacles.

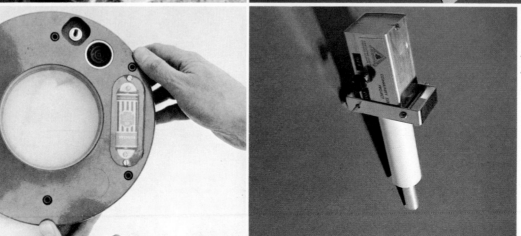

Left: Relaxation chair, counting rack and wooden rack for crutches for use in a special education center in Pennsylvania, developed by Pioneers for children with limited muscle control. Other though similar objects are in wide use nationally. Chairs were primarily designed for ELCODE system users.

Above: Wooden worktable with lock-in cabinet portion to hold erect physically handicapped children while they conduct tabletop activities. One of many Pioneer constructions used by the handicapped to improve educational training and recreational activities.

Right: Storage racks containing wooden teaching aids for retarded and handicapped children.

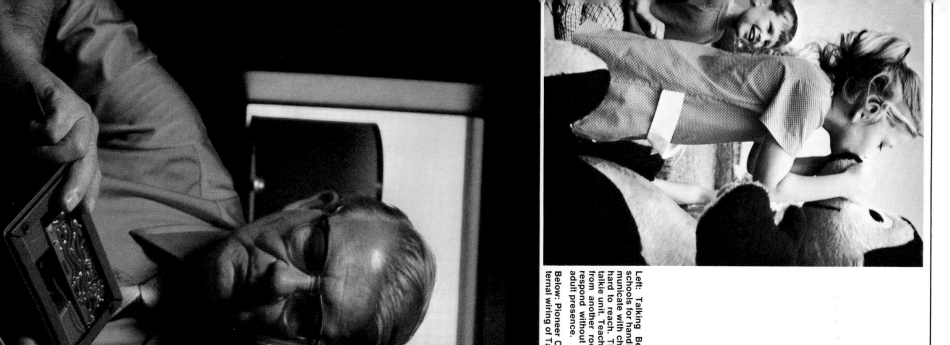

Left: Talking Bear — helps teachers at schools for handicapped and retarded and communicate with children who are particularly hard to reach. The dolls contain a walkie-talkie unit. Teachers talk "through" the doll from another room permitting children to respond without inhibitions caused by an adult presence.

Below: Pioneer C. F. Boettcher showing internal wiring of Talking Doll

Serving the Needy

Clockwise from top left: Pioneer John Lynch with Ring Toss, an audio game for blind children. A bowling pin is fitted with an electronic unit giving an audible signal. The child aims at the target. A buzzer trips when a "ringer" is scored. Pioneer handmade a knitted robe for convalescent patients; handicapped children playing with Pioneer-made rag dolls; children with Talking Doll.

Supreme Court in Washington; was the first president of the National Geographic Society, a Regent of the Smithsonian Institution, a member on the State Board of Education; made and lost several fortunes in street railways, gas lighting and other technological ventures; and was a driving force in the plans for the United States Centennial Exposition which later played a major role in telephone history. Hubbard's daughter, Mabel, was totally deaf from the age of five after a severe case of scarlet fever. Both men sought out the young Bell in their unstinting efforts to assist their beloved, handicapped children. Mabel Hubbard was rich and had everything possible done for her malady, including instruction in Germany where she learned lip reading. Yet her father was dissatisfied and unwilling to settle for sign language — the preferred system of

the time. He enthusiastically, if emotionally, agreed with Bell's view that oral training was both possible and more rewarding for the deaf. During the winter of 1872-73, Bell drove himself night and day, neglecting health. At night he performed electrical experiments with tuning forks, doing all mechanical work himself. During the day, he lectured and tutored pupils, including George Sanders. The pace could not last, and he returned to his forests at Brantford, physically and mentally exhausted. Before leaving Boston, he characteristically accepted a post for the following year as professor of Vocal Physiology and Elocution at the young Boston University. He also made arrangements to board with George Sanders' grandmother in Salem, where he could devote time to George's lessons, set up a workshop and commute to Boston. This

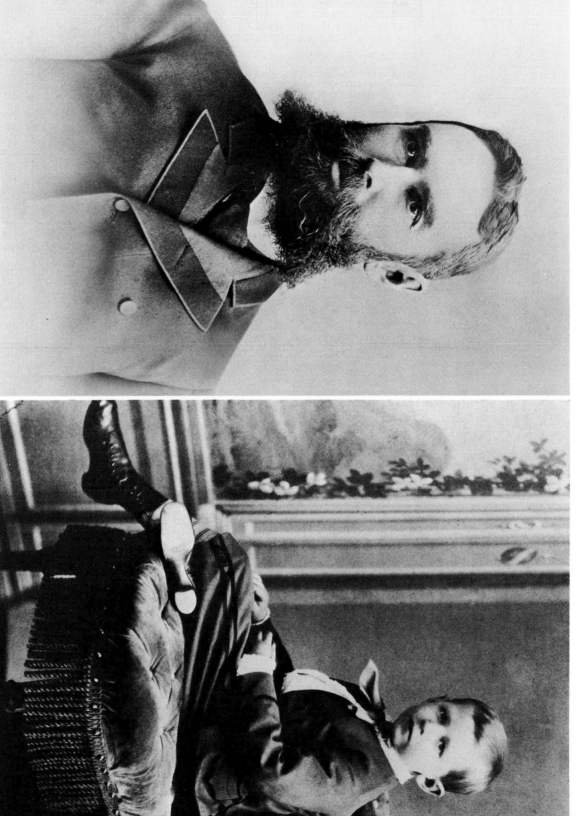

Thomas Sanders.

George T. Sanders. As a result of his training with Bell, he learned to communicate.

49

Gardiner Greene Hubbard

done, he went off to recuperate in the woods and on the waters of the Great Lakes. By October, he was living in Salem, fully recovered and anxious to resume the heroic routine.

"Talent is best nurtured in solitude." *Goethe*

His experiments were now leading to a "harmonic telegraph," which would undertake to transmit multiple, separate telegraphic messages over a single wire. The idea was simple, but the technology difficult and far beyond the state of the art of its time for reliable service. At the "sending" end, differently tuned tuning forks would generate tones which would be switched on and off by the usual telegrapher's key. All tones were placed in a jumble on the wire, like a simultaneous vocal quartet of soprano, alto, tenor and bass. At the "receiving" end, identical tuning forks would be tuned to respond only to their mates at the sending end, soprano-to-soprano, bass-to-bass, thus sorting out the garbled ensemble into the original, discrete messages.

His relationship with Mabel, now aged sixteen, began with observation and improvement of her lessons. (She thought

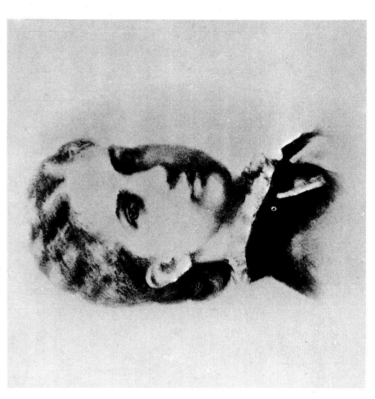

Mabel Hubbard (Mrs. Alexander Graham Bell). Reproduced from a crayon portrait of herself, made by her when 18 years old. Sketch made in 1875.

him something of a crank on their first meeting.) Amid the clinical advice on palates and diaphragms, Alec wrote one day as an afterthought in her notebook, "Your voice has a beautiful quality."

"My feelings and sympathies are everyday more and more aroused . . . it makes my very heart ache to see the difficulties the little [deaf] children have to contend with."
Bell on teaching, 1872.

He scored another triumph which brought him into contact with the scientific and intellectual life of Boston, much like his father's London experience. He lectured at the Massachusetts Institute of Technology on Visible Speech. The audience of four hundred included, in his words "the finest minds in Boston." He was granted use of the Institute's scientific apparatus, which included those of Helmholtz and the Phonauto-

graph, which displays speech in dynamic time patterns by tracings on smoked glass pulled rapidly past a membrane-driven scriber. He was welcomed as an associate by the M.I.T. acoustical scientists.

One of Bell's bizarre — but effective — contributions to the phonautograph was a device which used a human ear, procured for him by a friendly physician, where the bones formed the operating linkages. He was astonished at how the relatively heavy bones could amplify and reproduce so delicately the tiniest sounds. This encouraged him — unreasonably — to continue his research based on massive electromagnets.

Meanwhile, Bell intensified his efforts, prompted by the news of Elisha Gray's exciting, parallel experiments. At the time, Gray was the foremost "electrician" in America. Hubbard and Sanders were becoming interested in commercial

51

applications of the harmonic telegraph, and theoretical scientists encouraged him. Bell realized that he must abandon his solitary, secretive methods which were handicapped by his ineptness in precise manipulations. He needed expert mechanical assistance. Destiny here placed on his path that salutary encounter with Thomas A. Watson, completely unlike Bell in background, temperament and education. But their separate skills and mutual appreciation of each other's talents formed the most perfect match a benign Providence could design for their joint venture in making Nature unlock the secret which had eluded men since time began: the transmission of intelligible speech beyond the shouting range of human beings. It occurred in early 1874, in that atmosphere of urgency and single-mindedness which marked all their collaboration thereafter.

"A wise man turns chance into good fortune." *Thomas Fuller, 1732.*

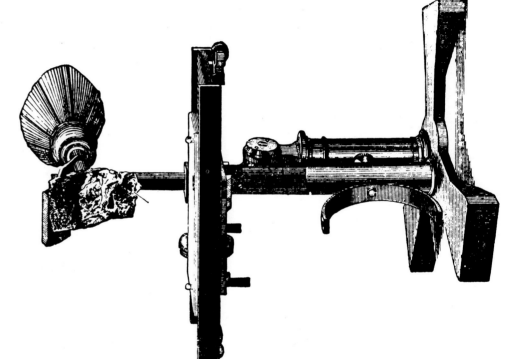

Late 19th century medicine advertisement. Until the second decade of the 20th century, there was no legislation prohibiting false claims in medical advertising. The practice of medicine was still primitive and the afflicted were at the mercy of the ignorant.

A drawing of the human ear phonautograph exhibited by Bell in a lecture on his experiments.

CHAPTER

4

4

HELPER EXTRAORDINARY: WATSON'S APPRENTICESHIP

Thomas A. Watson's charming autobiography is entitled *Exploring Life* and the title perfectly describes his attitude to the wonder of human existence. Curious, unpretentious, humorous, confident and adventurous, he epitomizes our idea of the "good sport," whose ebullience is never quenched by the random problems of life. His optimism was remarkable, even for a nineteenth century American. Ignorance of some subject is usually an embarrassment to most people. But Watson leapt fearlessly into any field he encountered the way an explorer or scientist of an unknown frontier plunges into domains which others prudently avoid. This happy-go-lucky quality joined to high spirits was of inestimable value to Bell's more elegant, restrained temperament. One can almost see in their collaboration a blending of the values of the Old and New Worlds, both learning from and sustaining the other.

CHILDHOOD: Watson was born January 18, 1854, in Salem, Massachusetts, above a large livery stable where his father was foreman. The stable was a major center of the town's life. Young Tom's father was on duty from early morning to late at night, seven days a week, available at any time he was needed. All members of the family worked at heavy tasks for long hours. Watson could not remember when he had not been employed. Water-carrying was a job he particularly disliked. Yet the place was full of romance for one blessed with imagination. His mother tried hard to bring a little beauty to its shabbiness with the morning glories he always remembered climbing on the unpainted walls. Nearly all unusual events required horses in those days. Tom witnessed the human

condition in emergencies, weddings, parades, funerals, elopements, intrigues, illnesses and parties from an early age and in all seasons — often riding on the box with the driver, serving as a miniature footman.

He felt his formal schooling, beginning at five, was almost worthless, even though it cost twenty-five cents a week. Reading became very important to him and furnished the materials for daydreams. But library charges and the requirement for economy forced him to read a book in one day, encouraging the habit of skimming which he deplored all his life. Yet the drudgery and want he experienced became a prime motivation to his continual pursuit and development of labor and time-saving devices which he hoped would lift some of the burden of the toil he had known at firsthand, or give increased opportunities for productive leisure and enjoyment.

In 1865, Abraham Lincoln was assassinated; the 13th Amendment abolishing slavery was added to the Constitution; Jefferson Davis was arrested and imprisoned.

At eleven, he found a job delivering crockery after school and worked until nine in the evening. Then he worked at assembling paper boxes, but he left it to become a salesman in a ready-made clothing store, while still attending school. Finally, at fourteen, he wished to contribute full-time to the small income of his family. He left school, becoming a salesman in the crockery store. Seeing no chance for advancement after a year (he made five dollars a week), Watson took a six-month commercial course in Boston, commuting by train, and continuing to work afternoons, evenings and weekends. He believed that he learned more in those six months, even

Watson's mother, Mary Phipps Watson.

Watson's father, Thomas Russell Watson.

though limited to bookkeeping, penmanship, arithmetic and commercial law, than in all his previous schooling. Yearning for a Boston position, he found that clerical work had harmed his eyes (he suffered from myopia but did not know it until later) so he decided to learn a trade. Carpentry lured him, but the strain of ten-hour days, handling large roof timbers and kegs of nails, showed his muscles to be weak. After padding about with odd jobs, he finally found exactly what he wanted: the Boston electrical machine shop of Charles Williams where he started on July 1, 1872, at the ripe age of 18. Watson did not know it at the time, but his life had taken a fateful turning.

MACHINIST: The shop occupied the third floor and attic of a dingy loft building and employed about twenty-five men. Twenty hand lathes, two engine lathes and hand tools made up its total equipment. Brass, steel, lumber and rough castings lay all about. One central sink ministered to cleanliness. A tiny office, partitioned from the men, handled clients' meetings and displayed apparatus models. Such small shops, scattered about the United States, made up the entire electrical industry of the age. The only practical use of electricity then was in telegraphs, burglar alarms and annunciator systems. Williams' workers made the apparatus involved, starting with raw metal and wood.

Advice of a noted inventor to Watson (1872), **"Never use an electrical device if you can find a mechanical one . . . Electricity is mighty uncertain stuff to work with."**

Watson early acquired a reputation for speed and quality. Because he disliked making repetitive runs of the same piece, he sought ways to minimize motion. He also developed special tools we know today as "jigs" and "fixtures" for turning out

Watson's store, 414 Essex Street, Salem, Massachusetts. Photographed about 1862.

Court Street, Boston, 1860's.

Electrical apparatus of the period. △

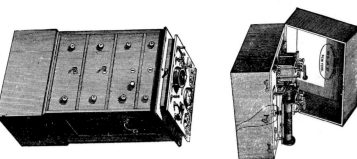
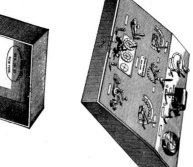
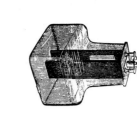

identical pars with precision and ease, the essentials of mass production. Watson's emphasis on motion study anticipated the ideas of scientific management which emerged only a generation later. At the end of two years, commuting daily from Salem, early morning and late evenings, Watson was a full-fledged journeyman. He was assigned the most complex and original jobs and made immune to layoffs when demand slackened.

During this period, he also pursued his interest in spiritualism with a boyhood friend who possessed psychic powers. Tom became disillusioned with organized religion after being subjected to excessive Sunday school "hell-fire and brimstone," but he maintained throughout his life a deeply religious strain. He continued to believe in reincarnation to the end of his life and developed sophisticated ideas on psychic phenomena. During a dramatic breakdown, his friend lost his power to conduct seances and engage in "automatic writing" on slates.

Watson said later that even as a member of The Society for Psychical Research he had never seen psychic power so strongly manifested as in Salem. Years later, baffled by a technical problem, he consulted a Boston medium for inspiration. Significantly, Watson was never bothered by scoffing of his ideas, and said *be* would probably have been as skeptical if he had not experienced what he did. It illustrates his open-mindedness, belief in his own observations, and an eagerness to find a pattern of understanding and explanation of everything in Nature. To some extent, electricity is a "spiritual" subject — because we know it only in its secondary effects on our senses, when transformed into heat, sound, light or motion. In its early days, a sympathy with occult phenomena was not a disadvantage. In fact, a mind at home with mysteries and fascinated by the unknown was more likely to be useful than one known as hardheaded or practical — whose narrowness blanks out consideration of things that "do not make sense" to

Seance with magician looking at her crystal ball.

57

its fossilized experience.

He also made a collection of rocks and, dissatisfied with his powers of declamation, bought books of poetry which he recited in the woods and on the beaches. Already he was discovering that solitude was essential to his development. Occasionally, he would take off a day (without pay) when the beauties of nature or prospects of an uninteresting, tedious run of work were too much for him. His interest in electrical machinery was supplemented by a fascination with steam engines; and when work was dull at the shop, he built several small engines and boilers. This excursion in latent capacity was to be an important factor in later life.

"If I had been born in India, I might have been content to spend my life in meditation." *Thomas Watson.*

Meanwhile, his curiosity, skill and willingness brought more and more of the experimental work to his bench. Electricity's power was sensed rather than realized, and many men were concocting "inventions" designed to exploit it. Williams' shop became a Mecca for such people and their characteristic impatience made Watson their favorite because of his speed

Gatling Gun.

and accuracy. Yet so many of these ideas failed that Watson became both skeptical and desirous of improving his own theoretical knowledge. He saw that many of the inventors were unfamiliar with both previous works and books on the subject. He used the library and bought technical works. Later he said that was how he first learned that a little reading saved much time and money in working out an invention. Those who were learned seemed more successful to Watson, and he was always eager to work with them because they were tutors for his informal education.

Early in 1874, Watson was interrupted while working on a device for exploding submarine mines by electricity developed by one of his favorite clients and "instructors," Moses G. Farmer. As he wrote later: "There came rushing out of the office door and through the shop to my workbench a tall, slender, quick-motioned young man with a pale face, black side-whiskers and drooping mustache, big nose and high, sloping forehead crowned with bushy jet-black hair. It was Alexander Graham Bell, a young professor in Boston University, whom I then met for the first time."

Winston Churchill was born in 1874.

4

Machinery and construction of the Age.
Building the Hoosac Tunnel.

Machine drill in tunnel.

Nitro-glycerin converting room.

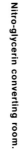

"Powder keg" battery and exploders.

West portal.

Bell had destroyed the discipline of the shop by penetrating to the workroom because his directions for building parts of the harmonic telegraph apparatus had not been followed correctly. Watson had worked on them during intervals on Farmer's apparatus, but had no idea what they were or to whom they belonged. Bell instantly explained his idea of the entire invention to Watson, who was then able to make the modifications intelligently and quickly. The first set of identically-tuned reed magnets worked perfectly on an improvised shop circuit. Yet when Watson built five more sets and Bell connected them all together, total failure and jumble resulted. Still, Bell was not discouraged and had Watson begin work on an "autograph telegraph" which would, Bell said, transmit handwriting and pictures, once the harmonic telegraph worked! This client-shop-mechanic relationship went on for several months without any practical success for Bell. But for Watson, acquaintance with the young, eccentric professor opened triumphal arches for his mind. He could not be the same man he was before that characteristic meeting, where real progress was made only by breaking the rules.

Thomas A. Watson, 1874.

60

CHAPTER

5

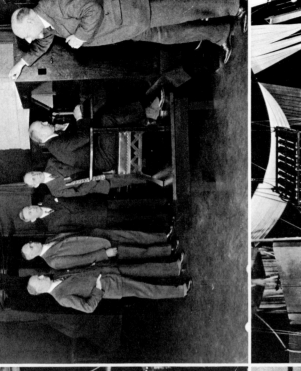

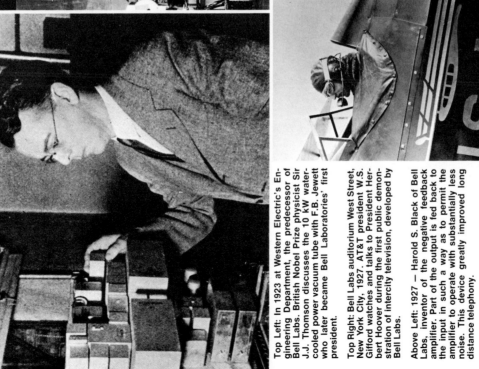

Top Left: In 1923 at Western Electric's Engineering Department, the predecessor of Bell Labs. British Nobel Prize physicist Sir J.J. Thomson discusses the 10 kW water-cooled power vacuum tube with F.B. Jewett who later became Bell Laboratories' first president.

Top Right: Bell Labs auditorium West Street, New York City, 1927. AT&T president W.S. Gifford watches and talks to President Herbert Hoover during the first public demonstration of intercity television, developed by Bell Labs.

Above Left: 1927 — Harold S. Black of Bell Labs, inventor of the negative feedback amplifier. Part of the output is fed back to the input in such a way as to permit the amplifier to operate with substantially less noise. This device greatly improved long distance telephony.

Above Right: Bell Labs Vice President E. B. Craft (black tie) Vitaphone studio of sound film in which he described Bell Labs innovations leading to the origination of sound motion pictures. One year later, "The Jazz Singer", the first feature film with synchronized dialogue, was made using Bell Labs techniques.

Top Left Clockwise: Capt. A. R. Brooks, Chief Pilot, Bell Labs, shown wearing newly devised helmet for use in two-way radio telephone communications.

Bell Labs equipped the first of several "Flying Laboratories" in 1928 to improve development and research in aviation radio.

Radiotelephone Laboratory, Deal, New Jersey. In 1922, after tests with coastwise ships, calls were made between Bell System telephones and the steamer *America*, 300 miles at sea.

Early version of artificial larynx (1929). Developed at Bell Labs, it enabled thousands of people to regain some power of speech. In 1960, an improved transistorized instrument was introduced.

1920's

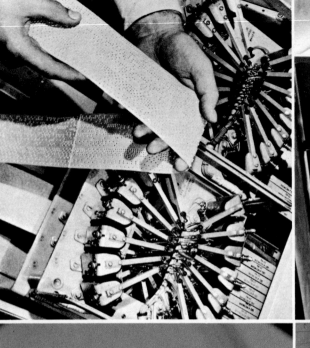
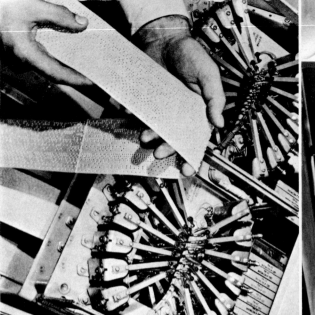

Right: The ELCOVEE, floating sonar laboratory used by Bell Labs to test and demonstrate newly developed Navy underwater sound equipments under actual operating conditions in the 1940's. Many sonar devices for antisubmarine and prosubmarine use were studied and tested with this floating laboratory.

Below Clockwise: Claude E. Shannon's now-classic papers on information theory, published in 1948, quantified "information" and gave engineers a mathematics-based "benchmark" — a theoretical maximum of information-carrying capacity for any communications system. Here, Shannon is pictured with an experiment he devised in 1952 — an electrical mouse which finds its way unerringly through a maze, guided by information "remembered" in the kind of switching relays used in dial telephone systems.

John Bardeen, William Shockley and Walter H. Brattain (l to r) discovered the transistor effect in 1947. For this epochal invention, the three scientists shared the Nobel Prize in Physics.

The first laboratory transistor.

An automatic message accounting system (1949), the result of years of intensive development work at Bell Labs, it kept track of thousands of dial telephone calls, remembered who made them, what numbers were called, how long the conversation lasted, and then added and printed detailed charge information.

1950's

Below: Bell Labs' scientist Arthur Schawlow (left) and C. H. Townes, a consultant to Bell Labs, inventors of the laser. Here they are shown with equipment used during early development of masers and lasers.

Gas Laser. The illustration shows a modern experiment exploring the potential of lasers for high-capacity transmission systems of the future.

Below: Bell Labs scientist W. Lincoln Hawkins and Vincent L. Lanza discovered (1956) a formula for preparing additives that stabilize the plastic protective covering of telephone cables, with the potential for extending the life of telephone cables up to 100 years.

Center: R. W. Hamming of Bell Labs (left) originated (1950) error-detecting and error-correcting codes which endow computers with the ability to detect and correct their own mistakes. Hamming codes permit data to be stored, retrieved, and transmitted error-free and are routinely used in the computer industry.

Bottom: Bell Labs scientists D. M. Chapin, C. S. Fuller and G. L. Pearson in 1954 invented the silicon solar battery — an efficient device for converting sunlight directly into electricity. Here, Chapin demonstrates how sunlight, through the solar battery, can power a motor-driven wheel.

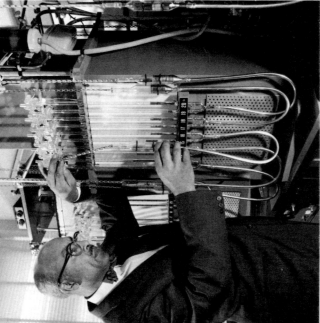

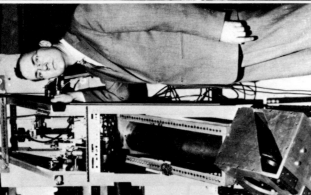

BELL TELEPHONE LABORATORIES: A Photographic Essay

The telephone invented by Alexander Graham Bell and Thomas Watson in the 1870's has been re-invented many times by an organization of uncommon creative genius: The Bell Telephone Laboratories. Founded in 1925, Bell Labs has given the world a remarkable array of scientific inventions which have re-shaped the life of the planet and our awareness of outer space. Bell Labs are an essentially "mission-oriented" research operation. Its "mission" is to analyze and anticipate the technological problems of the telephone as a communications device in all of its ramifications from operating companies and the inter-connections between them run by Long Lines. Working in a synergistic manner with Western Electric, Bell Labs, attempts to solve these problems.

"Great discoveries and improvements," Alexander Graham Bell once wrote, "invariably involve the cooperation of many minds.". He knew this well from his own experience of frustration working as an isolated inventor. He needed Watson's skills. It is a sobering thought that, had Bell and Watson failed to create the telephone, its invention would have come about inevitably.

If Bell Labs fails to research and develop concepts needed to maintain and expand the largest communications system in the world, one upon which hundreds of millions of people are dependent, the system will deteriorate and, ultimately, fail. Bell Labs responsibilities for the future is equally awesome, involves unbelievably complex technology but is within the tradition of Alexander Graham Bell himself — making it possible for one person to speak to another person over long distances quickly, inexpensively and reliably.

Right: 1886 — A corner of the laboratory of the American Bell Telephone Company at 141 Pearl Street, Boston. In that year, engineers proposed arrangements of wiring and coils making it possible to use four wires (two circuits) to carry three conversations and one telegraph message.

Harmonic telegraph receiver.

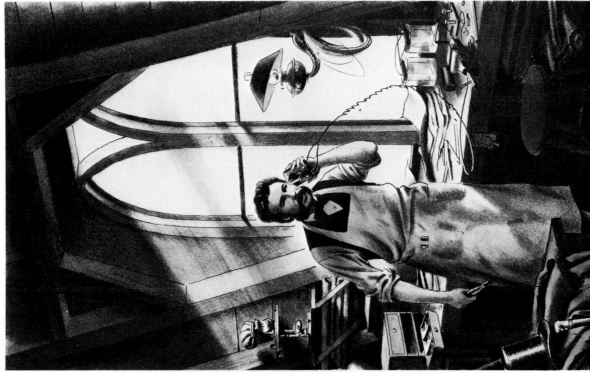

The design was simple but combined Bell's new knowledge with a mechanical version of the human ear. Watson made a small frame, shaped like a gallows, placed one of the harmonic telegraph reeds under it, but connected the end of the reed to a piece of parchment stretched like a primitive eardrum or tambourine. The idea was to aim your speech at the parchment, driving it into motion (like an ordinary drumhead) which would then cause the magnetized reed connected to it to wobble along with the parchment, making an electric current which, sent down the wire, would cause the reverse to happen: the current moving the receiving reed; the reed driving the parchment; and the image of the original sound heard by a listening ear held near the parchment. Simple, indeed, but the next night's work was discouraging.

Knowing that the attic was too small a distance for reliable tests, Watson hooked up a wire between the attic and his workbench after he worked all day building the instrument. However, it only worked faintly when Bell's powerful, resonant voice was used — and he shouted so loudly that he burst the parchment! Now began that process of exploitation of a tiny crack through the veil of Nature into a practical, robust device for the use of all. It has continued for the hundred years since that hot June night and those regiments of cool, sophisticated scientists and engineers who today labor in the bucolic acres of Bell Telephone Laboratories are the lineal descendants of those two raffish mechanics. One could choose far worse intellectual ancestors.

(Text continues on page 65)

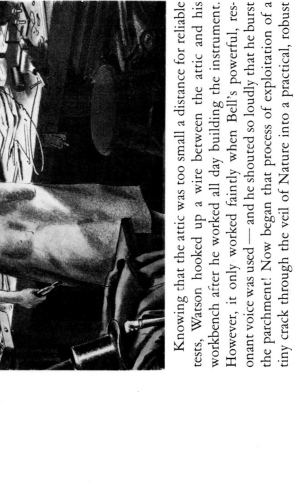

Illustration of Bell in attic at 109 Court Street, Boston, testing harmonic telegraph.

Harmonic telegraph transmitter.

5

AN EXPLOSION OF DISCOVERY: CHANCE AND NECESSITY

With the careless energies of youth, Bell and Watson pursued the will-of-the-wisp harmonic telegraph. Each day's assault, begun in zeal, ended with exhausted disappointment. They were like explorers lost in thick woods, hoping that every patch of open ground or sky leads to the haven of civilized settlement. Most inventors never find their way out. History ignores them, rewarding only success. Hope drives them on, but stamina and *recognized* luck also seem essential. Both men, happily, possessed all three.

On the hot afternoon of June 2, 1875, after two months of frustration and near-despair, they went up to work in the shop attic, because quiet was essential to "tuning" the matching reeds of the harmonic telegraph. This was a delicate job and only Bell's perfect ear was capable of it. Try to tune two guitar strings to the same note so exactly that one vibrates when the other is plucked and you get an idea of the problem. It is difficult enough with strings, but when you realize that Bell was attempting to do the same thing with rigidly clamped strips of spring steel, hovering over a crude magnetic coil, the idea verges on the edge of foolishness, if not madness. It would be easier to level a billiard table on a ship in a hurricane, by sawing off bits of each leg in sequence. The wonder is not that their frustration existed, but that they persisted in the face of all common sense.

In one room, Watson would send a vibrating current interrupted by his reed magnet to Bell in another room of the attic. Listening to the incoming tone (like a buzzing note) he would tune his receiving reed-magnet to it. Since the instruments were both crude and temperamental, constant tinkering was necessary by both men. In trying to get a more precise vibration, Watson turned an adjustment screw so tightly that the reed struck, putting everything out of action. He tried to restart it by plucking the frozen reed with his finger when he heard a loud shout from Bell in the other room. He rushed to Watson's side and excitedly pressed him to explain what he had done, because Bell had heard the *sound of the plucked reed* while impatiently waiting for the telegraph current to resume. Pasteur once wrote "Chance favors the prepared mind," and this incident, when Nature left the door to her secrets ajar for one instant, confirms his insight. Bell's vague, dreamy notion of how sound might be mirrored by an undulating electrical current, his hyper-normal sense of hearing, and the months of utter concentration which made him habitually and unconsciously press the reed-magnet to his ear, all combined to let him see the significance of an "accident" as though illumined by a bolt of lightning. He *knew* what had happened even though it would take many hours to articulate in words for others.

The end of June, 1875, Bell wrote to his parents: **"At last a means has been found which will render possible the transmission ... of the human voice ... I am close to the land for which I am bound and when the fog lifts I shall see it right before me."**

The two partners spent the rest of the night repeating the phenomenon with all the bits and pieces of hardware they could find. Before leaving, Bell had hurriedly sketched the plans for the first real telephone. He begged Watson to make it as fast as possible and have it ready for the next evening's work.

The "Gallows" Telephone (1875) a mechanical and electrical model of the human ear, used a vibrating membrane and a magnet to transform sound into electrical currents.

Bell in 1876.

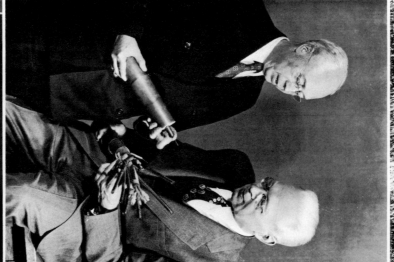

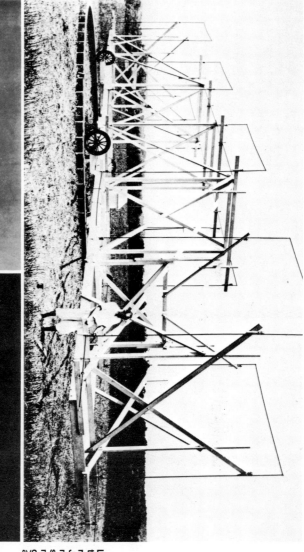

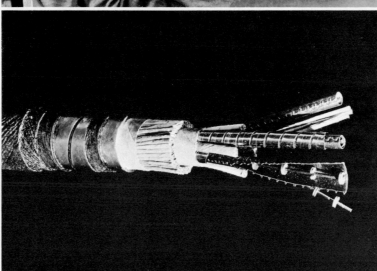

Left: Karl Jansky of Bell Labs is shown with the rotating antenna he used to discover radio waves coming from space. In 1933, Jansky's investigation into the strange noises affecting overseas radio-telephone service resulted in the discovery of radiation noise from the center of the Milky Way, and gave the world the new science of radio astronomy.

Far Left: Lloyd Espenschied (left) and Herman A. Affel hold early versions (1929) of coaxial cable for the wideband, long distance carrier transmission system they invented.

Left: Fanned-out view of the coaxial cable used in the first commercial installation in 1941. It had a capacity of 480 messages.

Far Left: The first electrical digital computer was the work of Bell Labs mathematician G. R. Stibitz who used telephone switching relays to design a relay digital computer (1937). With that computer, Bell Labs scientists demonstrated the first use of a remote computer terminal and data link in 1940.

Left: First electrically operated digital computer in the United States. The Stibitz computer featured remote, multiple access through three operator stations — one of which is shown above.

1970's

Below: Network managers use advanced computer techniques for dynamic control of the long-distance network.

Center: No. 4 Electronic Switching System, or ESS, developed by Bell Labs in association with Western Electric at a cost of over $400 million. Operated by Long Lines Department of AT&T. Network switching of pulsed codes representing speech signals takes place to a large extent in all-electronic form.

Bottom: Light-Emitting Diodes (LED) — solid state lights — are finding many telephone uses where their reliability and low power consumption help telephone companies hold down equipment repair costs and save electrical power.

Below: Computer-based business information systems are used by employees in many aspects of the telephone business, from customer service arrangements to inventory control for plug-in circuits.

Center: Linguists and engineers have made substantial progress in synthesizing human speech by electronic means.

Bottom: Ions are implanted in semiconductor materials to change their molecular nature and produce the electronic properties desired.

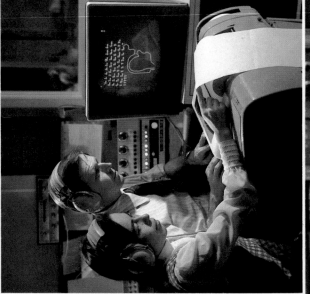

Above Left: Microwave towers throughout the nation are the workhorses of the transmission network, carrying the bulk of long distance calls, TV programs and other telecommunications.

Left: Systems for defending the nation against enemy missiles designed and tested by scientists and engineers at Bell Labs and Western Electric.

Top: "They're receiving us in Europe!" Eugene F. O'Neill of Bell Labs displays "thumbs up" as TV transmission to France via the Telstar[TR] experimental communications satellite is confirmed (1962).

Above: Communications satellites, pioneered at Bell Labs with the Echo and CSC Telstar[TR] experiments, recently introduced into the domestic telecommunications network.

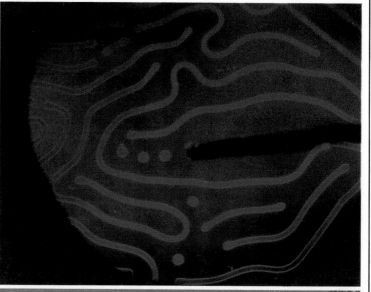

The Future

Right: March 10, 1976, on the 100th anniversary of the first complete sentence spoken over the telephone, AT&T demonstrated in Boston an exploratory development — telephone communication by light pulses through cables containing hair-thin, glass fiber light guides, each fiber guide able to carry hundreds of voice channels.

Below: Experimental millimeter waveguide transmission system: the most precise "pipes" ever manufactured may one day provide a communications superhighway for nearly half a million conversations at one time.

Below Right: Magnetic "bubbles", discovered at Bell Labs, show promise as extremely small, reliable memory devices for telecommunications and other consumer applications.

After a few weeks of frenzied modifications — which made the device "talk better" and remain in delicate adjustment — Bell's deep fear of the theft of his idea and his penchant for secrecy caused him to rent two attic rooms in a boarding house paying four dollars a week. He and Watson slept in one room. The other became their "laboratory" where they conducted all experiments for the next two years — until patents and public use of the telephone were established. During the last half of 1875, Bell once again became ill. While recovering at his father's house in Ontario, he wrote the specifications for his patent, which he filed on February 14, 1876. The patent was granted on his birthday, March 3, 1876, and officially issued on March 7. The clearness of expression and the underlying comprehension of the phenomenon evidenced in the patent application ultimately made it invulnerable to the unprecedented challenges and litigation caused by hundreds of opportunists

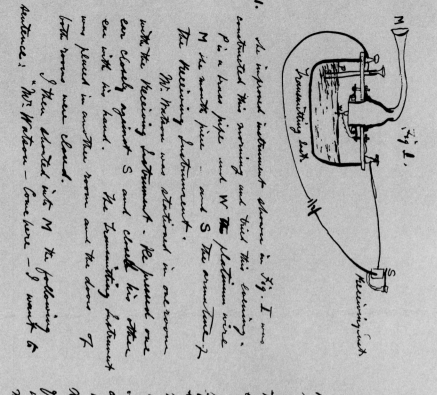

1. The improved instrument shown in Fig. 1 was constructed this morning and tried this evening. P is a brass pipe and W the platinum wire, M the mouth piece — and S the armature of the Receiving Instrument.

Mr. Watson was stationed in one room with the Receiving Instrument. He pressed one ear closely against S and closed his other ear with his hand. The Transmitting Instrument was placed in another room and the doors of both rooms were closed.

I then shouted into M the following sentence: "Mr. Watson — Come here — I want to see you." To my delight he came and declared that he had heard and understood what I said.

I asked him to repeat the words. He answered "You said 'Mr. Watson — come here — I want to see you.'" We then changed places and I listened at S while Mr. Watson read a few passages from a book into the mouth piece M. It was certainly the case that articulate sounds proceeded from S. The effect was loud but indistinct and muffled.

If I had read beforehand the passage given by Mr. Watson I should have recognized every word. As it was I could not make out the sense — but an occasional word here and there was quite distinct. I made out "to" and "out" and "further"; and finally the sentence "Mr. Bell do you understand what I say? Do — you — un — der — stand — what — I — say" came quite clearly and intelligibly. No sound was audible when the armature S was removed.

Specifications for patent.

eager to claim a stake in his success.

Though the principle was now secured by patent, no fully intelligible sentence was transmitted by telephone until March 10, 1876. The rapid succession of dates attests to the hectic pace of idea, device, development, testing, abandonment, rethinking, new idea and so on in a spiral-like dance of progress carried on at whirling speed. It is little wonder that Bell suffered periodic illnesses, almost in the nature of strategic retreats from efforts carried beyond human limits.

Bell and Watson perceived that, unaided, the human voice directly converted to electricity by moving magnets alone would impose intolerable limits on distance and clarity. They experimented using the voice vibrations to *control* a larger source of power derived from batteries which could be increased at will. This required the voice to vary the current in ways parallel to the air pressure differences we know as "sound." Watson built a device which used a small wire connected to the diaphragm at one end and suspended in diluted sulfuric acid at the other, much like a continuous "switch," which, instead of turning "on" or "off," would vary its resistance as it rose and fell in the cup of acid. The battery current in the wire to the receiver would rise and fall, vibrating the receiver membrane at the other end, producing sound. (This concept of variable resistance is still used in telephone transmitters today, though with material safer than sulfuric acid!)

With that peculiar mixture of manual clumsiness and mental sensitivity so characteristic of him, Bell sat down before the new instrument in the "laboratory." Watson connected the batteries and went off to the bedroom for the test. As he put the receiver to his ear, Watson was astonished to hear, with perfect clarity, "Mr. Watson, come here, I want you!" Watson laconically notes that "the tone of his voice indicated he needed help!" He rushed to Bell and saw that he had spilled sulfuric acid all over his clothes. Three aspects of this incident are noteworthy: the strict, Victorian formality of Bell's "Mr. Watson" after months of fraternal associations; Bell's instinctive use of the primitive telephone to summon aid in what

"Hello, Boris? Listen, Comrade Zherkov has invented something.... No, no, I mean *really* invented something!"

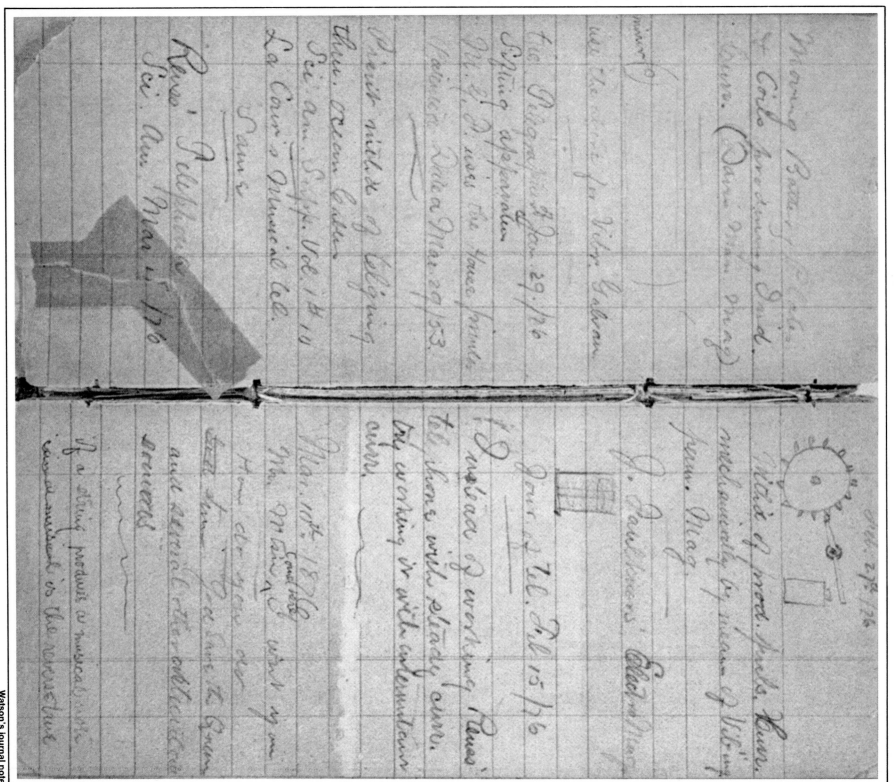

Following page ▷
Court Street workshop, a replica constructed with the advice of Thomas Watson. Now
on permanent display at the headquarters of
New England Telephone, Boston.

must have been a somewhat disconcerting accident; and the first practical use of this now-everyday instrument as an emergency call for help. No high-sounding phrases before distinguished audiences, as the "What hath God wrought?" of Morse's telegraph. Bell avoided historically selfconscious rhetoric used by heads of states. Instead, *a simple plea from a human being in trouble* attended the telephone's entrance as a social force. No more appropriate and symbolic event could be imagined or invented. That fact alone augured well for tapping the latent demand of human beings to bind themselves in a new conception of "community." Something truly *new* had

entered the world, not simply a clever assemblage of bits of wood and metal. It was an entirely novel form of "social glue."

On an average day in 1976, Long Lines Department handled over twelve million inter-state telephone calls.

Life for millions would not be the same after this tiny drama in a Boston attic. Again, symbolically, the inventors' energy burst the bounds of their laboratory when they erected the first outdoor telephone wire of half-a-mile over the housetops between the boarding house and Williams' shop. Long nights of intense solitary listening made them acquainted with all the mysterious noises and vagaries of interference which later

Workshop tools. Bell relied on Watson's mechanical ability to perfect the telephone.

Liquid telephone model disassembled on △ rough working drawings.

70

required the most penetrating research and creativity to conquer. The air and earth were full of electrical commotion and they were the first to experience its scope and wonder with their toy-like gear. Watson in later life thought the noise similar to radio static, and if so, they had been unwittingly linked to phenomena of cosmic origin whose ultimate nature is still a mystery.

However, opportunity and the urgency of the moment forced aside such lofty speculations. The imminence of the Centennial Exposition to be held in Philadelphia was a chance Bell could not ignore. Would they be prepared in time? What if failure attended wide public exposure of their "infant" to the rigors of jealousy and criticism?

In 1974, a coaxial cable between Pittsburgh and St. Louis operated by the Long Lines Department had the capacity to carry 108,000 conversations simultaneously. Bell Labs, Western Electric and Long Lines are working on a millimeter waveguide system to carry 500,000 conversations simultaneously.

Critical materials in perfecting the telephone: storage batteries, the gallows and centennial telephones.

CHAPTER

6

"Hold mere money cheap. It is not the finding of a thing, but the making something out of it after it is found, that is of consequence." *J. R. Lowell (1871)*

CENTENNIAL SUMMER: A RIPENESS OF TIME

While recuperating in Canada in those last months of 1875, Bell's life was far from that of a normal convalescent. Coincidence and drama — though fully documented — now carry one beyond all bounds of fictional invention.

Bell was plagued by financial worries. He was stung by his inability to pay petty loans. His teaching income was lost by concentration on the telephone. Hubbard harassed him to work on the harmonic telegraph and abandon telephony, but his anguish was relieved partially by his love for Mabel Hubbard. Yet he had no prospect of supporting a wife accustomed to the comfortable life her father's wealth provided.

In desperation, he struck on the idea of selling an interest in the telephone patents to be granted outside the United States. However, Great Britain's laws prohibited the granting of patents on devices previously patented in another country. Bell's dilemma was rooted in timing and sequence: if he filed first in the United States, there would be no British patents for sale to backers in Canada; if he waited to file first in Britain, he would be vulnerable to others who heard of his work and who might file contesting patents ahead of him in the United States. This accounts for his preoccupation with secrecy during 1875. He felt entangled in nets and snares. Ill at his father's house, Bell sought out George Brown, a powerful Canadian newspaper publisher and leader of the Liberal Party. Bell sold him an interest in the foreign patents for twenty-five dollars a month, in order to pay his small debts and substitute lecturers for educational commitments he was now unable to fulfill. Because Brown constantly delayed payments, Bell taught new students to give the lectures and set underway a burst of promotional activity to secure them paying students — a characteristic bootstrapping operation. He endured that most excruciating agony of a poor, proud man waiting for a rich one to make up his mind. Feverishly writing the specifications, giving a copy to Brown for his trip to London for filing there, and returning to Boston with the precious document, Bell found himself in November 1875 at the door of Hubbard's house, which was opened unexpectedly by Mabel. He instantly proposed marriage. She accepted. When Hubbard heard of the delicately-timed arrangements, his shrewd lawyer's instinct made him press Bell to place a copy of the specifications with an attorney in Washington who would file the papers as soon as Brown had done his work in London. This was a wise move. The frenzied nature of Bell's conduct at the time is seen in a piece of evidence in the court trial of his patent priority. Replying to an invitation from Pennsylvania to give a lecture on education of the deaf, he declined in a note written on a discarded sheet of the specification draft! Retrieved later from the school's files, it established beyond doubt the date of his reduction of ideas to the ponderous technical prose of patent procedure.

Meanwhile, in London, Brown, now removed from the hypnotic persuasion of Bell, succumbed to doubts of the telephone's practicability. He feared the ridicule of fellow businessmen and never took the specifications from his luggage!

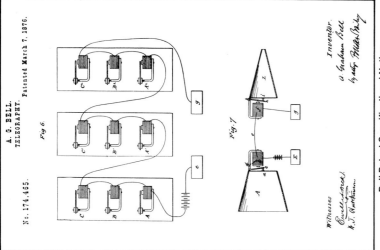

Bell Patent Specifications' Notice.

Hubbard, now suspicious at the lack of news, instructed the Washington attorney to file the application at the U.S. patent office. This was done on February 14, 1876, without Bell's prior knowledge — and not a moment too soon. That afternoon, a few hours after Bell's registration, Elisha Gray, the foremost "electrician" in America, filed a caveat on his prospective invention of a telephone. While technically only a warning to others, and not a true patent application, the entire history of the greatest patent litigation in history may have been far

Land circular inviting settlers to come to the Middle West in the 1870's.

Alec and Mabel, a few years after their marriage. Melville Bell wrote to his prospective daughter-in-law: "Alec . . . will make an excellent husband. He is hot-headed but warm-hearted — sentimental, dreamy, and self-absorbed, but sensitive and unselfish. He is ambitious, to a fault, . . . I have told you all the faults I know in him, and this catalog is wonderfully short."

Elisha Gray.

different, had Bell followed Gray. The consequences for its subsequent development would have been profound. As it was, the alternative courses of the telephone systems of the United States and Great Britain can be seen to have their origin in the different patent situations attending their legal births. Benign and mellowed by worldwide recognition, Bell, in later life, forgot or forgave all those who had opposed or harmed him with but one exception: George Brown. The psychic scar of the politician's mindless cruelty was indelibly marked on Bell's consciousness. Brown never knew it. He was assassinated by one of his own newspaper employees four years after his shabby treatment of the young inventor to whom he had sent only one installment of his promised twenty-five dollar monthly payments.

"The last hundred years have been the most fruitful and the most glorious period of equal length in the history of the human race . . . We are entering a year which will be ever memorable in our annals." *New York Herald January 1, 1876*

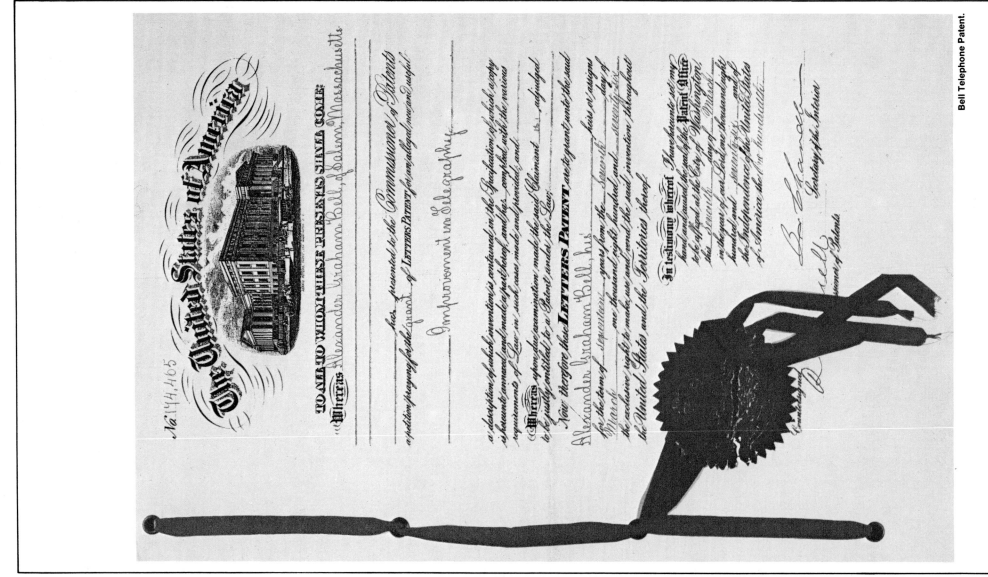

Bell Telephone Patent.

Custer's Last Stand, from a contemporary lithograph. On June 25, 1876, General George Armstrong Custer and his 200 soldiers were wiped out by Sitting Bull at the Little Big Horn River in Montana. The Indians were hoping to stop American prospectors and settlers in their sacred Black Hills.

Sioux account of Little Big Horn by a contemporary artist, White Bird.

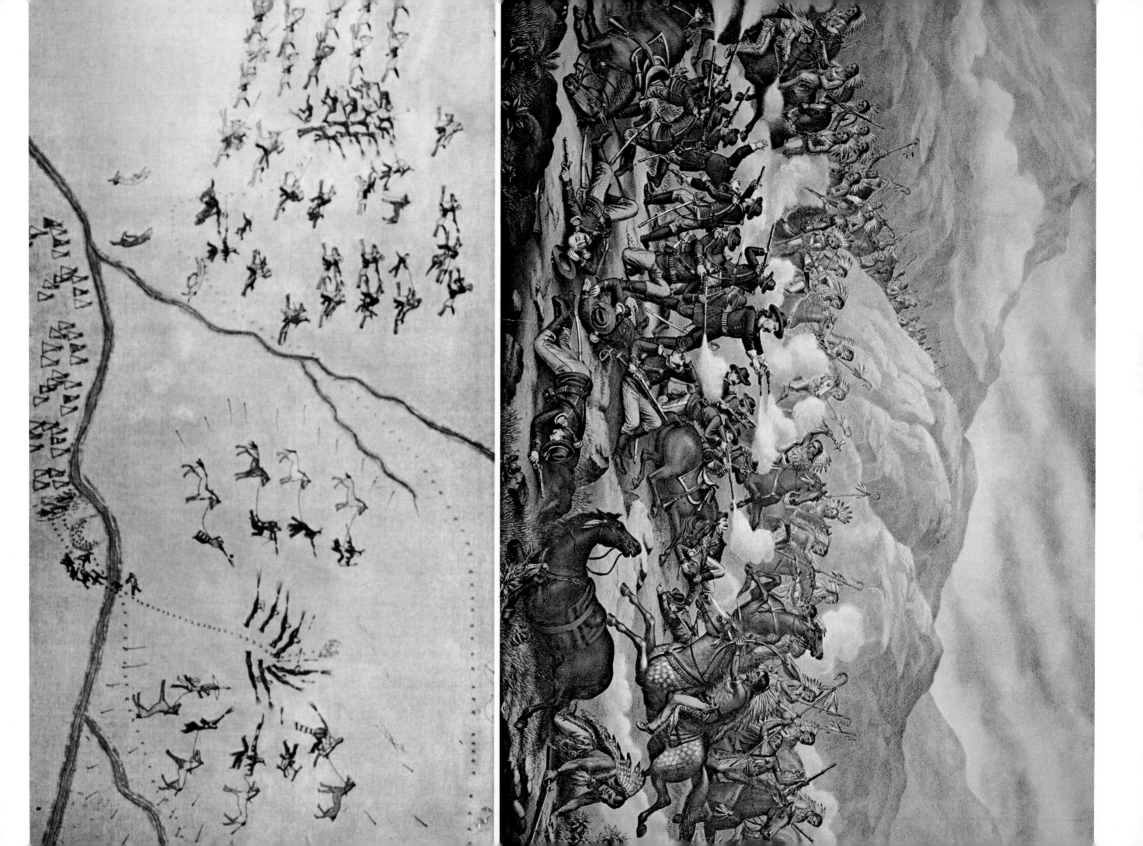

General view of the Centennial Exhibit. President U.S. Grant opened the Exhibit May 10, 1876. Six months later, the Exhibition closed having been viewed by ten million people.

"The Progress of the Century." Currier & Ives lithograph, 1876.

Women's rights champions Susan B. Anthony (1820-1906) and Elizabeth Cady Stanton (1815-1902). On July 4, 1876, a number of women's rights activists attended the Centennial and presented the "Declaration of Rights of the Women of the United States." They protested against "usurpation of power over women, in direct opposition to the principles of just government, acknowledged by the United States and its foundation." One anonymous suffragette said, "This government is not a Republic but a hateful oligarchy of sex."

PHILADELPHIA: It is impossible for our blasé age to catch the fever of the nation's first centennial celebration. Indifference has overtaken the innocent faith in progress which characterized the nineteenth century. The London (1851) and Paris (1855) Expositions had set the format: a vast site; experimental architecture; and international exhibits of fine and applied arts, science, industry, technology, coupled with unique aspects of history and culture. The fairs had become social and educational events, first-class instruments for decreasing provincialism, a superb communications system for leaders and

Centennial Fourth of July, 1876 Independence Hall, Philadelphia.

Grand trophy in the East end of the main building, illustrating the growth of the American flag.

This Exposition, too, had its king — a man perfectly cast for the role of royal guest of honor to a democratic nation: Dom Pedro II, Emperor of Brazil, the last leaf on the vestigial branch of that Portuguese empire which had first set in motion the Age which discovered America. The Emperor arrived early — with three battleships and a retinue — and stayed late in performing his expected duties with zest, curiosity and intelligence. The entire country caught "Centennial" fever. Celebrations of every kind, from rustic fairs to debutante cotillions, symposia and sermons appropriated the adjective to grace any gathering of that year.

Into this explosive social mixture, Bell casually struck his creative spark. On June 14, Dom Pedro visited Boston to inspect educational methods and met Bell there at a School for the Deaf. Visible Speech captured the imperial enthusiasm. A few days later, Hubbard, one of the three committee members of the Exposition, found a small place for Bell's work on Visible Speech in the Education Section. Bell had not planned

workers in specific fields, and a general stimulus for increasing recognition of industrial excellence and advances. The mixture of "establishment" figures from government, industry and society, along with artists, scientists, craftsmen, hordes of curious, wide-eyed visitors and continuous reportage by newspapers and magazines, made the celebrations a real force in the last century's consciousness. Awards and medals won there were proudly displayed on the labels and letterheads of those products honored by international panels of judges: from sauces and perfumes to gigantic industrial engines and printing presses. In that age of burgeoning democracies, the accolades of kings were thus gradually supplanted by the blessings of experts. But the kings still had roles to play — elegant promenades and the sense of the occasion were as much features of a great fair as the artifacts lavishly gathered and displayed.

"Rather than expend money for a jubilee in 1876," a New York Congressman said, "we should bequeath to our posterity the privilege of celebrating the continued existence of the Republic in 1976."

to attend the Fair. Hubbard urged his prospective son-in-law to hurry to Philadelphia with multiple telegraph and telephones for demonstration before the expert judges of electrical entries who were already assembling to inspect the exhibits on Sunday, June 25. The greatest expert was Sir William Thomson, later ennobled as Lord Kelvin, the foremost physicist of his day

Brazilian Emperor Dom Pedro and President U.S. Grant started the 1500-horsepower Corliss engine opening the Exhibit. The Emperor was the first Chief of State to visit America while in office. △

Bell's pass at the Exposition. He attended only one day, Sunday, June 25, 1876, when the grounds were closed to the general public.

and a leading member of the world's scientific Establishment. Bell hesitated, for two reasons. He had scheduled his school examinations for June 26th. He was also troubled by the question of conscience in not having applied for entrance to the Exposition before the official period had expired in April. However, love laughed at bureaucracy. Seeing how pale and anxious Mabel was at his unbending attitude, Bell impulsively boarded the train carrying her to meet her father. Taking no chances, Hubbard met him in New York and finally installed him in the Philadelphia hotel where the judges resided. There Bell met two of the judges and, on June 21, visited Kelvin as he was inspecting Elisha Gray's apparatus. After protracted conversations, conducted with Scottish accents on both sides, Kelvin said that he would examine the telephone on his official round with Dom Pedro on Sunday, the 25th. Bell agreed with misgivings. His apparatus was arriving from Watson, piece by piece, some of it damaged. But he kept on doggedly and wired young Willie Hubbard, Mabel's cousin, to come on as assistant. Willie arrived late Saturday night, in the nick of time. Sunday was a tropical day, and since it was the Sabbath, all exhibits were closed to the public. The emperor's party of fifty, including many notable scientists behind Kelvin, made their rounds burdened by fatigue and perspiration. Bell liked to

recount how the inspecting group planned to stop for the day before coming to him in another building. He was not in the Electrical Hall, but in an obscure corner, up a flight of steps. Still the indefatigable emperor, recognizing his new friend from Boston — the teacher of the deaf — swept the weary group to their duty. With Lord Kelvin at the receiver and Elisha Gray watching with Dom Pedro, Bell retired to his transmitter in the Main Building, a hundred yards away. Kelvin listened, the box pressed to his ear, and suddenly jumped up, shouting: "Mr. Bell! I must see Mr. Bell." He ran to the other end of the line where Bell kept repeating: "Do you understand what I say?" Out of breath, Kelvin said that he understood. He asked Bell to recite more. He ran back to the receiver. There, Dom Pedro sat astonished as Hamlet's soliloquy came from the metal cylinder. He exclaimed: "I hear, I hear." As the distinguished crowd took turns listening to the "magic," Elisha Gray ironically heard, "Aye, there's the rub."

Lord Kelvin (Sir William Thomson, 1824-1907). Kelvin made contributions in mathematics and physics, made contributions in message transmission by submarine cable, contributed to thermodynamics, introduced the Kelvin for absolute scale of temperature.

Bell's rival later said that when he repeated Hamlet's famous words to the audience, "they cheered." Kelvin was so excited he insisted on further experiments. He wanted his wife to see and hear the marvel. Bell pledged the services of Willie, and after a pleasant conversation with Gray about uniting their multiple telegraph interests, he left for Boston to conduct his pupils' examinations. A few hours after the demonstration the Canadian geologist, Hunt, wrote Bell telling him that Kelvin declared the telephone "the most wonderful thing he has seen in America" and was enthusiastically propagating this opinion to his scientific colleagues. The next day Willie Hubbard moved the exhibit to the judges' pavilion, where Kelvin and

Bell's "iron box" receiver of the centennial model phone.

A rare photograph of Bell instructing Dom△ Pedro on use of the Centennial phone receiver.

his wife ran back and forth between the instruments "like delighted children." The excited scientists made so much noise that the police feared a fire had broken out. Willie, a friend indeed, sent off a wire to Bell in Boston: "Sir William is entirely satisfied with the experiments. Never was more successful. A large number of sentences understood."

"Invention breeds invention." Ralph Waldo Emerson, 1870

For the first, and only, time, Bell and Hubbard neglected the public relations aspects of their work. Their confused uncertainty may account for the lapse, but after such "glorious success," as Bell described it, either a mysterious silence or routine boiler-plate notices were all the effects to be found in

84

the daily press. Still, the slow fuses of the scientists' imaginations were alight. They sent the news on their tribal medium, word-of-mouth.

"Americans seem to produce and circulate better machinery, cheaper and faster than we do. They are all natural mechanics. Their workers like the hum of wheels turning . . ." *Foreign traveler (1894)*

Kelvin arrived in Boston July 12th. He spent that evening working with Bell in telephone experiments over telegraph office lines, using instruments Watson had made especially as gifts for the scientist. Kelvin remained impressed, but his wide acquaintance with electrical workers in all nations, his knowledgeable reports of their work relevant to Bell's, and his suggestions for lines of future efforts seemed to dampen Alec's spirits after the euphoria of Philadelphia. The Boston *Globe* commented on the experiments in a report of the physicist's

visit. At the end of the experiments, Bell presented the instruments to Kelvin, wrapped simply in brown paper. Stuffed into the great man's luggage for England, the damage they suffered would be a crucial factor in the future.

Characteristically responding to frustration and an excess of stimulation, a week later Bell packed his bags, filling them with examination papers and telephone apparatus. Then he fled home to Canada.

Within days, he began following Mabel's admonition to do one thing at a time and concentrate on the telephone. "Try the lines between Paris (Canada) and Brantford," she advised. He nailed stovepipe wire on fence posts for the quarter-mile from his father's home to the telegraph line. On August 10, he completed the first one-way long-distance call of eight miles. Those old professional elocutionists, his uncle and father, were heard for over three hours by Bell and a crowd of ebullient

Bell using an iron box receiver, listening to his uncle and others speak from Brantford, Ontario. From a painting by Canadian artist John C.H. Forster.

Bell speaking into the Centennial phone, △ 1876.

townsmen in Paris. Bell's instinctive touch again served him well. When the lines were first connected, all they heard were bursts of noise and static. After signaling, by telegraph, for the substitution of high resistance coils in both instruments, the speech came through clearly. This was the first step on that long, empirical road of transmission improvement, the end of which is still not in sight. Already, people's lives were being changed in subtle ways by the crude, toy-like apparatus. (Lewis McFarlane, the *telegraph* office manager, who granted permission to use the line, later joined the infant telephone business in 1879, and retired from it as Chairman of the Board of the

Bell Telephone Company of Canada in 1930.) It was during this period of wild maneuvering that Alec acquired a nickname from his Canadian neighbors: they called him "Crazy Bell." Years later, many shook their heads in wonder when honors, eminence and a grand estate had transformed him, in their eyes, into a Great Man.

The Presidential election of 1876 between the Democrat Samuel Tilden and the Republican Rutherford Hayes was disputed, both parties charging bribery and corruption. Hayes was finally declared President by a Special Commission.

Late August 1876, Bell and Watson returned to Boston and began a series of experiments — more in the nature of wild forays — to improve the instruments. During Bell's absence, Hubbard offered Watson a tenth interest in the Bell patents if he would give up his job at Williams' shop to devote all his time to the telephone. Watson pondered this proposition for weeks. He had a good position, earning three dollars a day and was in line for promotion to foreman. He finally signed the contract for half his time, at the same wages as Williams', plus 10 percent of the patents. Watson himself received over sixty telephone patents and believed one of them was worth more to the Bell backers than everything he received from the contract. He promptly moved his lodgings to Bell's boarding house where their round-the-clock work resumed.

They changed every element of the devices — magnets, coils, diaphragms, mouthpieces — making phones ranging from a three-foot diameter piece of boiler iron to one using the *actual bones of a human ear*. All worked, but, astonishingly, the one finally selected is very similar to that used today. On October 9, 1876, the first two-way long-distance call was set up between Boston and Cambridgeport, using the Walworth Company's telegraph line between their offices and the improved telephones. Watson arrived at the plant, was treated suspiciously by the watchman and after tracing a short circuit, which had caused Bell to nearly lose his voice in unanswered shouts, Watson acknowledged Bell's now familiar "Ahoy!" Watson reported that the watchman, listening but unimpressed, felt the whole operation a humbug. Arriving back at the lodging after carrying his equipment (wrapped in newspaper), Watson joined Bell in a war dance he had learned from the Canadian Indians. It was always Alec's favorite form of victory celebration. Their landladies were not enthusiastic and indicated their preference for attention related to overdue rent as a real sign of success.

REVELATION AND EVANGELISM: Today, scholars in all cultures discuss the phenomenon of "technological diffusion." In plain words this means, "How is a technical discovery transmuted into something for widespread and everyday use?" The telephone was one of the most rapidly diffused of all inventions in history. The ingredients that produced the effect were a collection of highly motivated individuals, gifted in diverse ways, and the tapping of a latent demand for individual communication of enormous magnitude. Each amplified the other, building up resonances of explosive dimensions. Three numbers indicate the pace: in May 1877, there were six telephones in commercial use; in November, three thousand; and by 1881, a hundred and thirty-three thousand. A quick tour of those early months shows how driven personalities, taking great risks with both their reputations and resources, were essential for great accomplishments. They probably still are.

Newspaper reports brought all sorts and conditions of people to Bell and Watson's "laboratory," from savants to lunatics. But continual effort on improvement reached a plateau, and in November 1876, both exhausted men seemed dry of all ideas. Watson, willing to try anything, remembered his early experiences with spiritualism, and picking a psychic from advertisements, went off for a consultation. When she disappointed him, he went to brood in the public library. Leafing through a book on telegraphy, he came across a description of a "quick-acting" magnet used in a printer, which replaced battery-powered coils with permanent magnets. Inspired, Watson ran

Excerpt from Boston newspaper account, October 1876, of long-distance telephone call between Boston and Cambridge.

Walworth Manufacturing Company, Cambridgeport, Massachusetts in 1876. Site of the first two-way telephone call in history, October 9, 1876. Bell called the event, "The proudest day of my life...marking the successful completion of Telephony...much doubtless yet remains to be done in perfecting details of apparatus."

TELEPHONY.

AUDIBLE SPEECH CONVEYED TWO MILES BY TELEGRAPH.

PROFESSOR A. GRAHAM BELL'S DISCOVERY—SUCCESSFUL AND INTERESTING EXPERIMENTS—THE RECORD OF A CONVERSATION CARRIED ON BETWEEN BOSTON AND CAMBRIDGEPORT.

The following account of an experiment made on the evening of October 9 by Alexander Graham Bell and Thomas A. Watson is interesting, as being the record of the first conversation ever carried on by word of mouth over a telegraph wire. Telephones were placed at either end of a telegraph line owned by the Walworth Manufacturing Company, extending from their office in Boston to their factory in Cambridgeport, a distance of about two miles. The company's battery, consisting of nine Daniels cells, was removed from the circuit and another of ten carbon elements substituted. Articulate conversation then took place through the wire. The sounds, at first faint and indistinct, became suddenly quite loud and intelligible. Mr. Bell in Boston and Mr. Watson in Cambridge then took notes of what was said and heard, and the comparison of the two records is most interesting, as showing the accuracy of the electrical transmission:—

BOSTON RECORD.	CAMBRIDGEPORT RECORD.
Mr. Bell.—What do you think was the matter with the instruments?	Mr. Bell—What do you think is the matter with the instruments?
Mr. Watson—There was nothing the matter with	Mr. Watson—There is nothing the matter with them.

to their rooms, built one from scraps in an hour, and mounted it in one of the "unimprovable" telephones. To his immense joy, the power and clarity were far enhanced beyond anything built earlier. The clouds of depression lifted like fog dispelled by the sun. Energies flowed with enormous vigor. On November 26, the new phones worked well on the sixteen miles of line between Salem and Boston. On December 3, Watson took the train to North Conway, New Hampshire, 143 miles from Boston. This was an incredible assault on Nature with bare fists. While professional lungs and ears allowed the two of them to blast an intelligible message through a primitive telegraph wire, it would take years of development — and devices undreamt of — before such lengths could be spanned by ordinary voices. But one result of that trip was to give Watson a fascination with mountains which he retained all his life. The 22-year old technician was another whose horizons were expanded beyond previous imagination by his association with the invention. When Bell told him that New Hampshire had only "hills," and that Switzerland was the place for real mountains, Watson's ambition for travel was sparked. At that moment, his preoccupation with telephony diminished. Thereafter, he saw the telephone simply as a means to realize a full life, not as an end in itself.

"One touch of nature makes the whole world kin."
Troilus and Cressida.

Foreign artist's account of America in 1876. Note the top panel "Hard Times" depicting disappointed immigrants returning to Europe. Foreign critiques of America's relative prosperity and individual freedom made the United States a constant source of envy and abuse.

CHAPTER

7

7

FROM IDEA TO INSTITUTION: THE ENTREPRENEURIAL EPOCH

In their amateurish way, Bell and Watson were stumbling from the world of experimental science into the domain of engineering. In that land, harsh winds of finance buffet any who cross its frontiers. Naïve inventors were often destroyed when they exposed the children of their minds to the chilling climate of commerce. Bell was luckier than most. An experienced Yankee lawyer, Gardiner Hubbard, took from Alec burdens he could not carry and served him with both honesty and brilliance.

All of the experiments, traveling and demonstrations required money. The scale of effort soon exhausted the personal fortunes of both Hubbard and Sanders, the leather merchant whose deaf son was Bell's pupil, and whose generosity was remarkable in any age. *In the autumn of 1876, Hubbard offered all Bell's patents to the Western Union Telegraph Company for $100,000!* Fortunately, the proposal was contemptuously refused by the president of the great communications enterprise. Watson was disappointed. He saw 10 thousand exciting dollars — his 10 percent share of the Patent Association — disappear, as well as his position as superintendent of the telephone portion. But, as Watson said later, "It was a piece of good fortune for us all."

The Algonquin Indians accepted $24 for Manhattan Island in 1626.

Denied the quick route to financial independence, the group had to fall back on their native resourcefulness. Bell was truly desperate for some kind of income to support his marriage to Mabel. He quickly filed the patent for the "box telephone" (combination transmitter and receiver, quick-acting magnet and metal diaphragm) on January 15, 1877, and it was issued on January 30. This was the second — and last — of the fundamental patent foundations and represented the final technical contribution Bell was to make to telephony.

But he had yet to make one penny from his exhausting labors of invention. His genetic heritage of platform presence again rescued him. After giving a free lecture on the telephone in Salem, he sensed a deep public demand for dramatic scientific demonstrations. On February 12, 1877, he repeated the Salem lecture, this time charging an admission fee, earning eighty-five dollars — which he promptly spent on a silver model of the phone as a gift to Mabel. This event also saw the first newspaper story reported by telephone — by an old classmate of Watson's to his paper, *The Boston Globe.* This unexpected source of income marked a crucial turn in the financial evolution of the industry. Mrs. Hubbard, eager for Bell to become financially secure in order to marry Mabel, strongly urged that the primitive telephones be made in large numbers for direct sale to users. Without the windfalls of his popular lectures, Bell and Hubbard could not have maintained their vision of *creating and selling a total service system* rather than merely retailing isolated instruments.

The following months were filled by demonstrations in Boston, Providence and New York. Using the riskiest of homemade devices, they rented public halls and transmitted, via rented telegraph wires, over remarkable distances. Watson assembled a kind of oral vaudeville show presided over by Bell

The First Commercial Telephone, 1877. The round, camera-like opening served as transmitter and receiver requiring mouth to ear shifts. It went into service in 1877 when a Boston banker leased two instruments which were attached to a line between his office and home in Somerville, Massachusetts.

7

Early Telephone Booth standard from 1890 to 1900. Graciously outfitted with rugs, lace curtains and fancy cabinet woodwork, it was sturdily built with double walls and a domed roof.

First public exhibition of the telephone in Salem, Massachusetts. Top: Watson talking from Boston, explaining the invention to reporters and scientists. Below: Bell in Lyceum Hall, Salem, demonstrating the new device.

on the platform. The awestruck audiences, sitting under several telephones suspended from ceilings, heard conversations between the two collaborators which triggered cornet and trombone solos, choral works, organ music and songs bellowed by Watson with titles like *Hold the Fort, Yankee Doodle, Pull for the Shore, Auld Lang Syne* and his sentimental favorite, *Do Not Trust Him, Gentle Lady.* Watson modestly wrote that the imperfections of the instruments gave his steam-organ voice, developed by months of shouting in the laboratory, a mystic quality which always brought calls for encores.

After one of these demonstrations, with Bell in New York and Watson in their Boston bedroom-laboratory, their landlady complained about the noise. Watson then was forced to invent something we now hardly notice: the telephone booth. He made a tunnel of barrel hoops covered with blankets,

crawled inside and sweated through his repertoire, exhausted but unheard by neighbors. All attempts to escalate musical quality by employing professional singers failed. Watson remained the undisputed virtuoso of the new art form for its entire, though short, life.

The current Guinness world record for people squeezed into a Bell System phone booth is: 88.

Now reasonably prosperous from telephone demonstrations, Bell married Mabel on July 11, 1877. On August 4, the couple left for England on their honeymoon. When he returned, fifteen months later, Bell's technical and management involvement with the telephone business ended of his own choice.

Meanwhile, Hubbard and Watson applied themselves to commercial development. Hubbard organized companies and

CITY HALL, LAWRENCE, MASS.
Monday Evening, May 28

THE MIRACLE

WONDERFUL TELE P HONE DISCOVERY
TELE HONE OF THE AGE

Prof. A. Graham Bell, assisted by Mr. Frederic A. Gower, will give an exhibition of his wonderful and miraculous discovery The Telephone, before the people of Lawrence as above, when Boston and Lawrence will be connected via the Western Union Telegraph and instrumental music and conversation will be transmitted a distance of 27 miles and received by the audience in the City Hall.
Prof. Bell will give an explanatory lecture with this marvelous exhibition.

Cards of Admission, 35 cents
Reserved Seats, 50 cents
Sale of seats at Stratton's will open at 9 o'clock.

"Wonderful Discovery of the Age", an advertisement for a Bell lecture-demonstration of the telephone in Lawrence, Massachusetts, May 28, 1877.

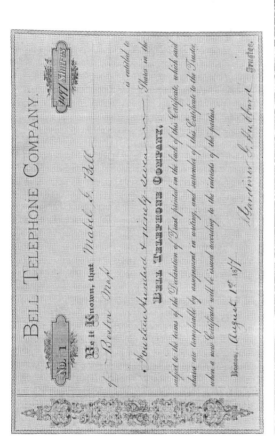

Stock Certificates for two of the seven stockholders in 1877: Thomas A. Watson and Mabel Bell. By 1976 there were over three million shareholders in the Bell System.

Vail, age 16.

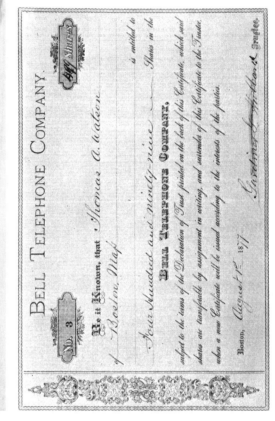

Birthplace of Theodore N. Vail in Malvern, Ohio, July 16, 1845. The photograph shows the house without the porch or wood siding.

7

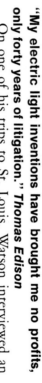

Emile Berliner (1851-1929), inventor of loose-contact telephone transmitter, disk phonograph record and a method of mass-producing phonograph records. He later began experiments in helicopter construction.

licensees. Watson arranged for supplies of apparatus, and made necessary inventions, like ringers and switchboards, almost casually in the course of meeting problems of turning a laboratory curiosity into a public service.

The Bell Telephone Company was organized in July 1877 by Hubbard, Williams' shop manufactured telephones to Watson's order. By November, three thousand instruments were generating income. They hired a bookkeeper in August to assist Watson — the company's single employee.

While Bell was traveling, lecturing and promoting in Europe, the pace in America was explosive. Fierce competition arose from those who wished to seize the fruits of Bell and Watson's work before they could do so themselves. The Western Union Company, realizing their error of judgment in rejecting Hubbard's offer, began selling telephones throughout the country, ignoring the Bell patents. By 1878 Watson made several extensive trips across the country to offer technical advice to the new licensees and to observe the effects of Western Union's campaign against the infant Bell enterprise. Edison, at the height of his powers, had produced a carbon transmitter which was supposedly bought by Western Union. Licensees soon reported its use. Watson set out to better its performance, *even though Edison appeared to infringe on Bell's patents.*

"My electric light inventions have brought me no profits, only forty years of litigation." *Thomas Edison*

On one of his trips to St. Louis, Watson interviewed an acquaintance of Hubbard's, Theodore N. Vail, who was superintendent of the Post Office's Railway Mail Service. Favorably impressed with him but unsure as to how they would get him to abandon a secure job paying $4,500 (!) per year, Watson recommended an offer be made Vail. A few days later Vail accepted, becoming the Bell Company's general manager at $2,500 per year, plus a $1,000 bonus if his performance was satisfactory. *This was probably the most momentous personnel decision in the history of the Bell System.* It illustrates how the serendipity of highly motivated individuals, available at the right time, seems to have attended the Bell System's evolution over the years. When Vail took power in July 1878, there were only 10,755 telephones in service. But the character of the American telephone industry was set for its future journey into greatness.

By 1976 there was more than one telephone for every two Americans: about 145 million telephones, 220 million people.

While on his 1878 travels, Watson also visited Emile Berliner, an immigrant dry goods clerk in Washington, who had invented a carbon transmitter. After testing it, Watson recommended purchase. Berliner was hired as a technical expert in Boston. He made great contributions to commercially suitable telephone apparatus, especially on the transmitter brought to Watson in October 1878 by Francis Blake — which proved to be more than a match for the Edison threat. In the complicated patent suits of the next twenty-five years, all these highly-charged individuals — and many more — played a part. Bell himself, a master of forensics and absolutely certain of the details of his highly documented work, was one of the most impressive witnesses ever to grace a courtroom. We take their success for granted, but in those hectic early days, it was a "near run thing."

Watson, taking charge of engineering, assembled a small corps of technical workers dedicated to what we now call

(Text continues on page 97)

Bell once remarked that fortunately he was not a trained electrician. An electrician might never have invented the telephone believing the concept to be too remote for practical realization. But without Watson's hardheaded electrical craftsmanship, the telephone might have remained an abstract idea, not a concrete thing. Vail was neither an inventor nor a craftsman. He managed what Bell and Watson created. He applied, in an efficient way, this "electrical toy". The interdependence of these three men may be considered analagous to the Bell System. For example, Bell Laboratories are concerned with the discovery and invention of new devices, the creation of new knowledge, Alexander Graham Bell's lifelong ambition. Western Electric is the "Watson" of the triad, concerned with manufacturing processes and products. The operating companies and AT&T are the "manifestations" of Vail, unable to reach their potential for excellence without the "Bell" and "Watson" roles. Western Electric, like Watson himself, is the most complex element in the telephone story. It manufactures and services the equipment needed to operate the Bell System. It supplies as well the paraphenalia of everyday operations — from pencils to paper. The largest employer in the System, it has manufacturing plants nationwide and takes the entire network as its customer, North and South, East and West. Using inventions perfected by Bell Laboratories, it creates defense and space equipment. It all began in the 1870's in the small Boston workshop of Charles Williams, where Bell found Watson, forming that indispensable partnership needed to create the telephone.

Left: In the early 1870's these 49 men were the entire personnel of Gray and Barton shortly to become, in 1881, the Western Electric Manufacturing Co. The gentlemen in the beaver hat (center) is Elisha Gray, holding his printing telegraph instrument. Enos M. Barton stands second from left third row.

Right: The new headquarters on Clinton St., Chicago, 1883.

WESTERN ELECTRIC: A Photographic Essay

Manufacturing

Below: Early Chicago Factory Scene — Stranding Department, Polk Street cable plant, Western Electric Company around 1890.

Right: Cable manufacture at Phoenix, Arizona Works.

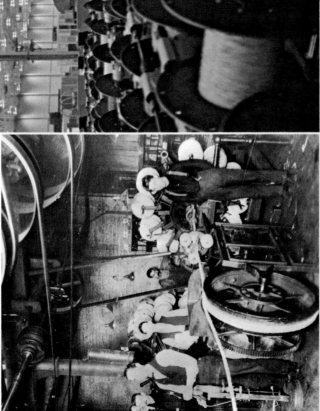

Top left: Light-emitting diodes are produced in Reading, Pa. The diodes will eventually replace conventional filament lamps because they are smaller, more reliable, and use less power.

Top right: Integrated Circuit Chip. A silicon crystal which re-creates all electronic circuits. Developed by Bell Labs, the Bell System uses these Chips, manufactured by Western Electric, for switching and transmission purposes.

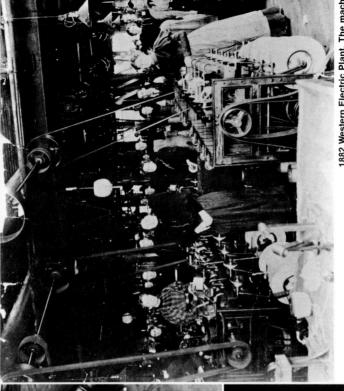

1882 Western Electric Plant. The machinery was considered complex for its time.

Right: Denver, Colorado manufacturing plant of Western Electric.

Front right: Substrates, part of a tone generator used in Touch-Tone® Trimline® telephone sets, are removed from a gold evaporation chamber at Western Electric's Indianapolis plant.

Above left: Transistor — invented by Bell Labs, manufactured by Western Electric.

Cutting laser used in Allentown, Pa., in a high-speed, computer-controlled system to contour-saw ceramic substrates for microwave integrated circuits.

Above: A 1913 newspaper advertisement for non-telephonic home utilities manufactured by Western Electric.

Top right: September, 1936: Amelia Earhart, wearing her Western Electric headphones, keeps in touch with ground stations as she manipulates the instrument-board controls of her "flying laboratory." The radio equipment was developed by Bell Laboratories, manufactured and installed by Western Electric.

Center right: A National Broadcasting Company mobile radio transmitter at the New York waterfront. Until the late 1930's, most network transmitters were manufactured by Western Electric.

Right: Norma Shearer, Metro-Goldwyn-Mayer moviestar of the 1930's, takes lessons in sound recording from her brother Douglas, chief sound engineer. Here he is showing her how the voice is photographed on films as it comes through recording channels in the form of electrical impulses. Western Electric, in association with Bell Laboratories, pioneered in the development of talking pictures.

Manufacturing

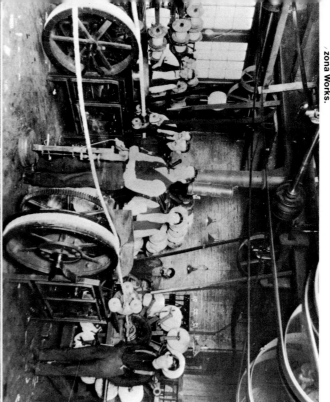

Right: Cable manufacture at Phoenix, Arizona Works.

Below: Early Chicago Factory Scene — Stranding Department, Polk Street cable plant, Western Electric Company around 1890.

Top left: Light-emitting diodes are produced in Reading, Pa. The diodes will eventually replace conventional filament lamps because they are smaller, more reliable, and use less power.

Top right: Integrated Circuit Chip. A silicon crystal which re-creates all electronic circuits. Developed by Bell Labs, the Bell System uses these Chips, manufactured by Western Electric, for switching and transmission purposes.

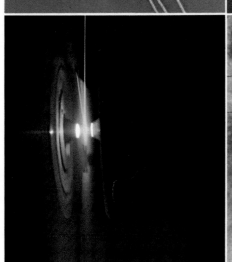

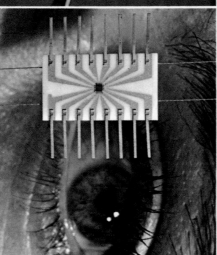

Above left: Transistor — invented by Bell Labs, manufactured by Western Electric.

Cutting laser used in Allentown, Pa. in a high-speed, computer-controlled system to contour-saw ceramic substrates for microwave integrated circuits.

1882 Western Electric Plant. The machinery was considered complex for its time.

Right: Denver, Colorado manufacturing plant of Western Electric.

Front right: Substrates, part of a tone generator used in Touch-Tone® Trimline® telephone sets, are removed from a gold evaporation chamber at Western Electric's Indianapolis plant.

Non-telephonic Items

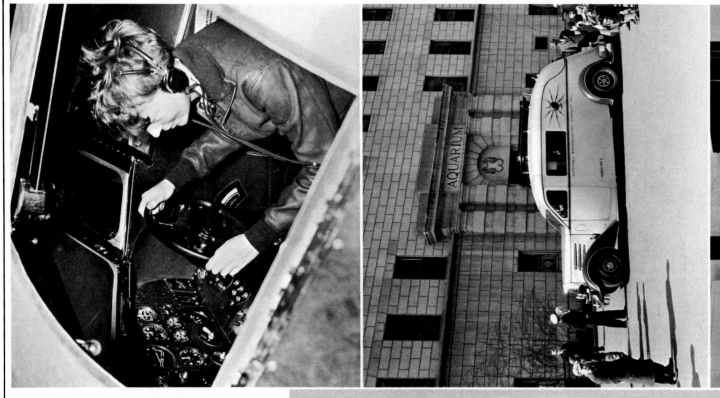

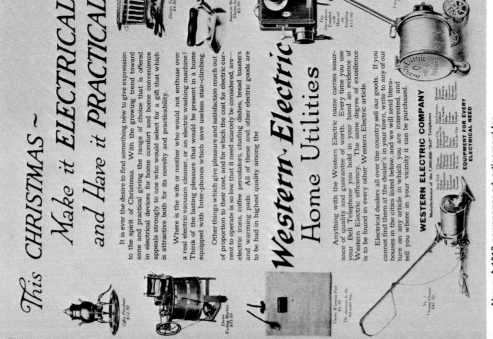

This CHRISTMAS ~
Make it ELECTRICAL and Have it PRACTICAL

It is ever the desire to find something new to give expression to the spirit of Christmas. With the growing trend toward sane and practical giving the range of choice that is offered in electrical devices for home comfort and home convenience appeals strongly to one who would select for a gift that which is attractive both for its novelty and practicability.

Where is the wife or mother who would not enthuse over a real electric vacuum cleaner, or an electric washing machine? Think of the lasting pleasure that would be present in a home equipped with Inter-phones which save useless stair-climbing.

Other things which give pleasure and satisfaction much out of proportion to their cost, and for which the cost for electric current to operate is so low that it need scarcely be considered, are—electric irons, coffee percolators, chafing dishes, bread toasters and warming pads. All of these and other electric goods are to be had in highest quality among the

Western Electric
Home Utilities

Anything with the Western Electric name carries assurance of quality and guarantee of worth. Every time you use your Bell Telephone you hold in your hand an evidence of Western Electric efficiency. The same degree of excellence is to be found in every other Western Electric article.

Electrical dealers all over the country sell our goods. If you cannot find them at the dealer's in your town, write to any of our houses in the cities listed below, and we will send literature on any article in which you are interested, and tell you where in your vicinity it can be purchased.

WESTERN ELECTRIC COMPANY
Manufacturers of the 7,500,000 "Bell" Telephones

EQUIPMENT FOR EVERY ELECTRICAL NEED

Above: A 1913 newspaper advertisement for non-telephonic home utilities manufactured by Western Electric.

Top right: September, 1936: Amelia Earhart, wearing her Western Electric headphones, keeps in touch with ground stations as she manipulates the instrument-board controls of her "flying laboratory." The radio equipment was developed by Bell Laboratories, manufactured and installed by Western Electric.

Center right: A National Broadcasting Company mobile radio transmitter at the New York waterfront. Until the late 1930's, most network transmitters were manufactured by Western Electric.

Right: Norma Shearer, Metro-Goldwyn-Mayer moviestar of the 1930's, takes lessons in sound recording from her brother Douglas, chief sound engineer. Here he is showing her how the voice is photographed on films as it comes through recording channels in the form of electrical impulses. Western Electric, in association with Bell Laboratories, pioneered in the development of talking pictures.

Aids For the Handicapped

An early carryingcase and hearing aid manufactured by Western Electric and used in the middle 1930's.

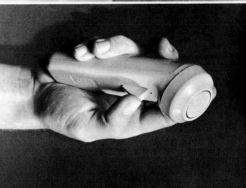

Electronic Voice — Sound is projected from the head of the Western Electric electronic larynx into the user's throat cavity, enabling him to form words with mouth and tongue almost normally.

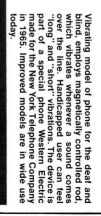

Vibrating model of phone for the deaf and blind, employs magnetically controlled rod, which vibrates whenever a sound comes over the line. Handicapped user can feel "long" and "short" vibrations. The device is part of a special phone Western Electric made for the New York Telephone Company in 1965. Improved models are in wide use today.

Defense

Center left: As wind-driven fog rolls across the Atlantic many miles off the coast of New England, a Texas Tower cuts a swath in its path. On board this radar island, Western Electric equipment helps to guard North America from a surprise attack.

Above: A complex electronic control system for guiding pilotless missiles to intercept high-flying enemy aircraft. Developed by Bell Telephone Laboratories, under a contract between the Western Electric Company and the United States Army Ordnance Corps. By means of intricate computing devices, which are the heart of the control system, enemy aircraft are detected and tracked by Bell Labs — Western Electric radar which feeds the computer information concerning the plane's altitude, speed and course. Aerodynamics and manufacture of the missile were handled by Douglas Aircraft.

Left: World War II Radar in Operation — draped with camouflage netting, this SCR-547 radar stood guard against the Luftwaffe near San Pietro, Italy.

Top: Telstar developed by Bell Labs, with guidance systems manufactured by Western Electric, launched by NASA.

Above center: Plastic sphere, 100 feet in diameter, of type used in Project Echo transmission experiments. In orbit, thin plastic with aluminized surface reflects microwaves. Western Electric manufactured the guidance systems.

Left: On April 1, 1960, a three-stage Thor-Able rocket launched the TIROS meteorological satellite into a nearly perfect circular orbit to observe and photograph global weather conditions. A Command Guidance System, developed by Bell Labs and produced at Western Electric's North Carolina Works, was used to direct TIROS into its orbit.

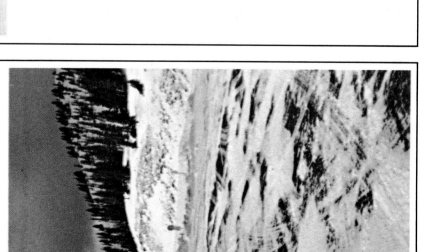

Top left: Installation of a board in Portland, Oregon about 1900.

Above: Installation of First Cosmic/Cosmos at Beverly Hills central office, California 1974. Uses computer techniques in switching.

Left: An "instant" Central office on a truck. 5A Crossbar installation at Hanover, Minn., 1972. The complete operation is done quickly in less than a day, using modular pre-fabricated elements. The two old men are now within 100 yards of a global communications point.

Below: WE installers set out by snowmobile to modify microwave systems at site atop the "Great Divide", altitude 12,000 feet. Monarch Pass, Colorado.

Supply

Right: A three-horse truck at Pittsburgh with a load of distributing wire. (1913)

Below: Material management center at Underwood, Iowa — one of seven in the nation — brings efficiency and economy to the task of resupplying working stocks maintained for operating companies.

Conservation and Recycling

Right: Nassau Re-cycling plant reclaiming copper, a subsidiary operation of Western Electric.

Below: Reclaiming materials for conservation.

research and development. Vail, as general manager, enthusiastically supported this continuous improvement effort, which has remained a tradition unbroken since its inception. They placed phones in mines, on submarine cables, on railroads, anywhere, any place, and welcomed each request, however eccentric, as a challenge. Watson even had himself lowered to the bottom of Boston Harbor in a diving suit because the phones he made for talking to the surface did not work. He solved the problem by falling on his face in the murk and mud below, which released an air pocket in the helmet, allowing operation. Returning to the dock, he instructed the divers to "make a deep bow" when talking — which they did!

Meanwhile, in England, Bell evangelized his invention and his visions of its potential throughout the technical and social institutions of the world. This period established his later fame. He was welcomed to the widest range of intellectual, cultural and scientific establishments. At a meeting in Plymouth of the British Association for the Advancement of Science, Lord Kelvin demonstrated the telephone by reciting: "Hey, diddle-diddle, the cat and the fiddle — please follow that up!" As he put the receiver to his ear, standing before the hushed assembly, his face lit up and he announced (to wild applause), "There he goes — he says, 'The cow jumped over the moon!'" Bell later asked Kelvin's assistant, a mile away, what had happened. He was told, "I did not hear him at all and said, 'Please repeat!'"

When business is good it pays to advertise; when business is bad you've got to advertise.

Anon.

An American journalist, Kate Field, conducted a brilliant publicity campaign, including a *Matinée-Téléphonique* presented at the opening of Parliament; published scores of articles; and succeeded in making the telephone the prevalent topic of conversation throughout London. Even Gilbert and Sullivan, in *H.M.S. Pinafore*, included the telephone in the lyrics of a quartet:

He'll hear no tone,
Of the maiden he loves so well!
No Telephone
Communicates with his cell!

Punch cartoons and scholarly reports led to a royal command from Queen Victoria who wished to see the wonder herself. The demonstration took place at her summer house on the Isle of Wight and was so successful that Her Majesty made an offer to buy the instruments for permanent use. Bell considered them too primitive for royalty, but it took so long to make new ones of carved ivory that the Queen lost interest. A priceless marketing lesson, not to be forgotten by generations of Bell's successors, was thus learned in the industry's infancy.

While in London, Bell wrote a remarkably prophetic report on the future of the telephone. It includes nearly every aspect of our modern systems: central offices, overhead and underground cables, long-distance lines, testing facilities, billing methods, public telephones, switchboards, inventory controls, sale of service rather than the instruments and wires themselves, prohibition against resale of services, the ambitious goal of a phone available to all in their homes and places of work, marketing strategies and publicity campaigns — all justified on the basis of the public good. Unfortunately, all the hardheaded recipients of the prospectus tore it up, many with a smile at the naïveté of such a utopian dreamer.

Queen Victoria in the 1880's.

7

One other strange occurrence marks the British phase of telephone history. Patents were denied because the public demonstration of Lord Kelvin, which took place before Bell's patent application, violated English patent rules. The matter was resolved in Bell's favor only because the hurried packing of the instruments for Kelvin in Boston had damaged them and made the diaphragm inoperable. So the instruments disclosed to the public were not the same as those submitted for the patent. All was well and justice was served!

In Britain the telephone was called the *voice telegraph*. Since the telegraph was a nationalized service, operated by the Post Office, an obvious Crown monopoly, the evolution of the telephone industry in England — and most other nations — was carried forward as a nationalized service. The American route, in contrast, was one of private enterprise with all risks borne by individual investors. Two divergent sets of traditions and goals for telephone service were begun from its earliest days. The privately owned American system aimed at the greatest public market and the widest use of the telephone, a reflection of a democratic mind. The foreign state-owned systems were founded in countries lacking egalitarian traditions. It is no accident that today, and from its beginnings, the greatest number of telephones in the world are in use in the greatest participatory democracy in the world. Bell, Watson and Vail were indifferent to class or ideology. The telephone itself did not discriminate against race, creed or color. It served lords and "commoners" equally.

Country and Population	Economic System	Number of Telephones
United States 220,000,000	Free Enterprise	145,000,000
U.S.S.R. (Russia) 260,000,000	Socialist	16,000,000

"Flying Machine", patented March 5, 1889. Thousands of esoteric patents were granted in late 19th century America, including many bogus devices.

Figure For Ballroom Dancing Practice, patented May 17, 1921, a handy instrument for getting in shape during the marathon dance craze of the 1920's.

The first three decades of the telephone's life display a tangle of complicated events and conflicts. They may be seen as a skein of three major strands, held together like a tight braid or cable, which conducted the course of the telephone as a social force in the life of the nation. The three strands were protracted legal battles over patent claims for the basic inventions; financing, building and manning an organization capable of rapidly bringing telephone service to a large and growing country; and finding solutions to a variety of technological problems which grew nearly as fast as the customer list. Success in each was necessary, but alone not sufficient, for a successful operating *system*. Failure in any one of the three would have doomed the entire enterprise.

In September 1878, the tiny Bell organization filed a suit against the giant Western Union Telegraph Company to protect Bell's patents against infringements by Edison and Gray, whose apparatus was used by Western Union. This was the first of more than six-hundred legal actions in a battle for the right to transform the invention into an industry. Twenty years and severe drains of scarce funds were necessary to defend Bell's claims. But he triumphed in every court of appeal as well as in the five cases decided by the Supreme Court itself. Bell himself, though his professional involvement with the telephone ceased on his return from England, was the most crucial witness in these actions. He worked tirelessly throughout the entire period, though the tedious fighting so repelled him that, until his death, he detested all aspects of commercial development of any inventions.

"He that goes to law holds a wolf by the ear." (1621)
"Laws are inherited like diseases." Goethe

The first suit resulted in victory. Western Union's chief lawyer advised surrender to Bell after he saw the evidence for both sides assembled in one year. Western Union's telephone interests and properties were acquired by the National Bell Company, the corporation formed in February 1879 to promote the invention by licensing to others. On the news of the settlement in November, its stock, originally issued at $110 soared to $995!

Other suits are of interest only to specialists, but one, begun in 1885, was filed in Tennessee by the Pan-Electric Company whose officials charged that Bell had secured his patents by fraud and collusion with Patent Office personnel. The Attorney General of the United States — who also happened to be a

major stockholder of Pan-Electric — sued Bell in the name of the United States Government. The suit produced a scandal which rocked the highest levels of government, precipitated a Congressional investigation, triggered an editorial war between two newspaper giants — Pulitzer and *The New York Times* — rose to the Supreme Court and resulted in complete victory for Bell in 1888.

Though viciously slandered as a result of hostility and envy he could never understand and continually harassed for documents and testimony, Bell refused to lower his high standards of gentlemanly behaviour in meeting unfair assaults on his character and work.

Now the invention and patents were secure; the company was organized. What next?

"Management" can be defined as the art of organizing, planning, directing and controlling both the skills of people and the resources they need to achieve a shared goal: continu-

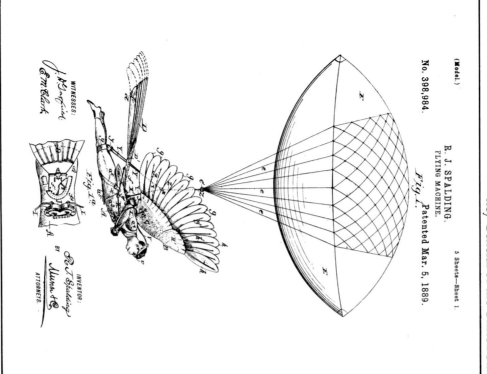

(Model.)

No. 398,984.

R. J. SPALDING.
FLYING MACHINE.

Fig. 1. Patented Mar. 5, 1889.

5 Sheets—Sheet 1.

WITNESSES:

INVENTOR:
R J Spalding
BY ATTORNEYS

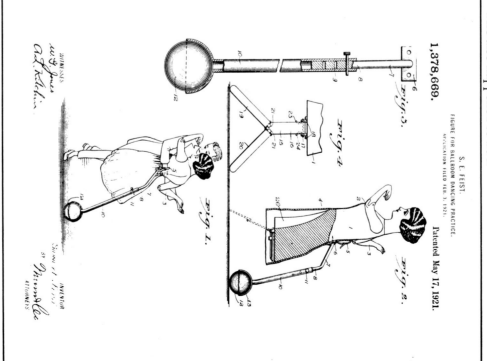

1,378,669.

S. E. FEIST.
FIGURE FOR BALLROOM DANCING PRACTICE.
APPLICATION FILED FEB. 3, 1921.

Patented May 17, 1921.

Fig. 3.

Fig. 4.

Fig. 1.

Fig. 2.

WITNESSES

INVENTOR

ATTORNEYS

ing success. Performance is judged by speed, quality and efficiency. Development of the telephone industry from its earliest days furnishes a textbook example of the management art. It also shows the indispensability of vision, energy, courage and tenacity in those who would practice the art — and the consequences of their absence.

Theodore Vail, the first general manager of the telephone business, brought managerial skill of an order close to genius in forging the organization needed to transform Bell's discoveries into a widespread social and economic force. No aspect of the present System is without the imprint of Vail's original thoughts and vigorous actions.

Within days of arrival, he fired off bulletins and orders on a Napoleonic scale, written in the confident, first-person style which characterized all his communications — even annual reports to stockholders. He assumed personal responsibility for

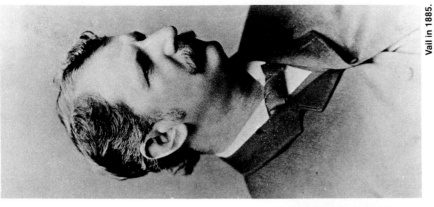

Vail in 1885.

Fireworks heralding the opening of the Brooklyn Bridge, May 24, 1883, a great American technological achievement.

A biting look at big business and monopolies at the turn of the century. Stimulated by these ideas, reformers demanded government regulation of industry and the launching of anti-trust law suits.

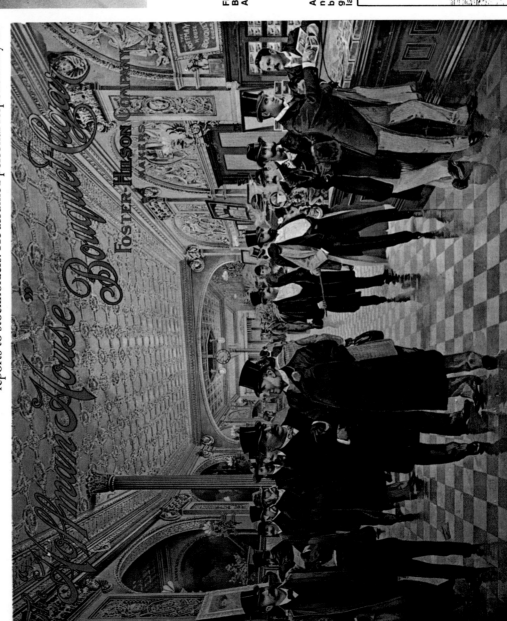

Inside view of the Hoffmann House, a famous New York restaurant of the 1880's. Political and artistic notables gathered there. Among those shown are: David B. Hill, railroad baron, Buffalo Bill Cody (in front of the column), President Grover Cleveland and the infamous politician Chauncey Depew.

everything. Vail was not a man of his own time: he was far in advance of it. Unlike the Robber Barons of finance of that age who saw the accumulation of money itself as the sole purpose of their lives, Vail looked on money as merely a resource whose only value was to advance the System. This break with the classic capitalist mind forced him to leave before his work was done and then return to the rescue when so-called "practical men of business" failed.

"In the land of the blind, the one-eyed man is often in the zoo." Adam Hall (1965)

Seeing what others were unable to see, the enormous potential for service, Vail knew that the only way to attract the funds nationally was to give Bell patent franchises to local businessmen in exchange for a share of their local stock. Licenses for the use of the patents — the method used by Hubbard to produce *some* income in the early period — pro-

vided only a temporary source of funds. The two basic patents would expire in 1893 and 1894. Besides, leaving local units to evolve in haphazard fashion without a vision as to how all the pieces of the nation's communications would blend into a real system was to contradict the logic of development. Every new telephone should add value and access to all others, so that the growth of the *system* could benefit *all* customers. Vail saw that, no matter how the tedious patent contests came out, much more was at stake: only an organization geared to deliver what people needed and wanted would be allowed to live. To seek immunity and protection for shortfalls in performance was a blind alley in the long run.

The patent association of Bell, Hubbard, Sanders and War-

son was like a mutual club. Then the corporate form of this "club," in the name of the Bell Telephone Company, required money far beyond the capacity of the members. In 1878, the New England Telephone Company was formed to sell licenses to operators in New England. This was superseded by the National Bell Telephone Company in 1879, which was to speed the licensing process throughout the country. Meantime, in hundreds of cities and towns, entities named the "Bell Telephone Company of such-and-such" were established for local service as they received their licenses. When Western Union sold its telephones to Bell, their operation combined with the National Bell was chartered as the American Bell in 1880 — and this remained the parent company of the present

Bell System until 1899. At the time of its creation there were 61,000 telephones in the entire country. By 1885 the need for an operating and engineering company that would tie all the other companies together — so that a customer of one could call any other person with a telephone — was obvious. Vail's original personal dream of a unified, interlocking system, now was the conventional wisdom.

The American Telephone and Telegraph Company — A.T.&T. — was chartered in New York, rather than in Massachusetts, the home of American Bell. Vail was president of A.T.&T., president of the Metropolitan Telephone and Telegraph, which serviced New York City, and general manager of American Bell. His brain combined the functions of parent company, long-distance company and local company. He acquired the manufacturing possibilities of the Western Electric Company in 1882. Technical research functions were carried on by Watson's collection of inventors. Vail fused all to make the telephone system of the United States more than the sum of its parts. By 1885, he created a tool uniquely suited for the titanic job ahead.

The charter of A.T.&T. reflected Vail's ideas: "... the lines of this association ... will connect one or more points in each and every city, town or place, in the State of New York with one or more points in each and every other city, town or place in said State, and in the rest of the United States, Canada and Mexico, and also by cable and other appropriate means with the rest of the known world as may hereafter become necessary or desirable in conducting the business of the association." By 1899, the rigidities and limitations of Massachusetts corporate concepts were constricting the expansion of the industry. American Bell was limited to $10 million of capital. Since the A.T.&T. Company — formed for long distance service — had grown from $100,000 capital to $20 million in just fourteen years, it was an obvious choice for the parent company of the System to absorb the functions of American Bell. At that time A.T.&T. total assets were $120 million. This merger was accomplished. The structure has remained to the present day.

After his herculean labor to build the organization needed, after recruiting the talented people to its service and after hammering out the doctrines of its long-run policy, Vail clashed with Boston financiers who saw the enterprise simply as a financial engine. American Bell's president, William Forbes, considered dividends far more important than service. Vail, by contrast, wanted every possible dollar put back into expanding the System in order to meet the explosive demand for service. He felt this to be the only sure way to ultimate success. His arguments and logic fell on ears deafened to all but immediate returns: Vail resigned in 1887 rather than compromise the most profound ideal of his life. In fairness to the Boston financiers, theirs was the wisdom of the time. Vail's notions struck them as radical and dangerous. And, indeed, they were. His ideas were the ideas of the future, and he would return, twenty years later as hero and savior.

In late 19th century America, the average housewife worked 17 hours daily, without pay.

John E. Hudson succeeded him. No greater contrast could be imagined. The robust Vail was a child of the American heartland — self-educated, itinerant telegrapher, symbol of the surging energies of a young nation, familiar with its frontier towns and at home with people in every walk of life; whereas, Hudson was a fastidious lawyer and scholar, who enlightened

First headquarters building of the New York Telephone Company, 18 Courtlandt Street, New York City, 1896.

The Johnstown Flood devouring the city in the Conemaugh Valley, Pennsylvania. May 31, 1889. One of the late 19th century tragedies, it underlined the forces at work needed to span the continent and attempt instant communications on a reliable basis.

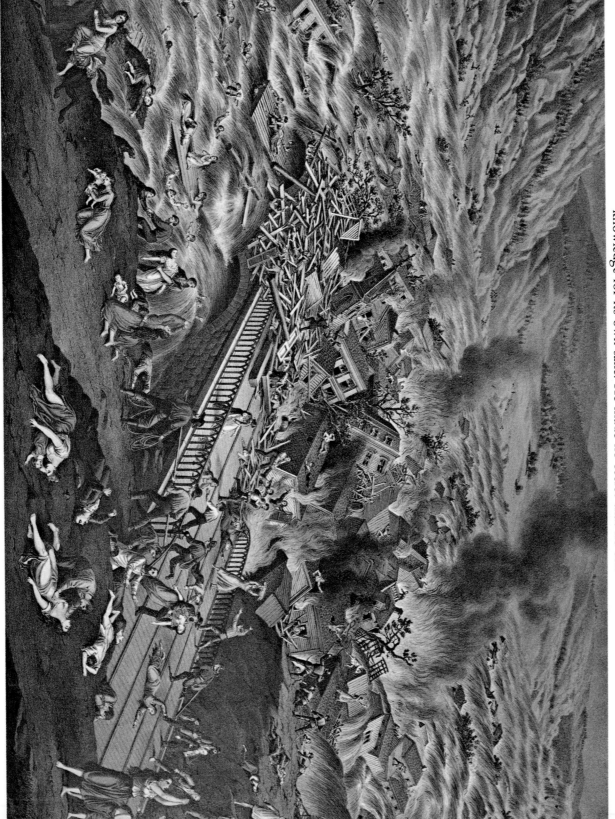

his colleagues by employing elegant office memos in classical Greek (though their substance was that of caution and conservatism). Furthermore, he had a particularly low opinion of inventors, whom he considered a raffish, extravagant and ill-disciplined lot. For twenty years the System survived perilously until Vail returned, his original idea vindicated.

"One machine can do the work of fifty ordinary men. No machine can do the work of one extraordinary man."
E. Hubbard

Thomas Edison, born in the same year as Bell, was the classic nineteenth century inventor. He once described the difference between science and technology. Scientists, he said, pursued knowledge for its own sake. He made no secret that he con-

sidered pure science mere foolishness and he had contempt for "theoreticians." Inventors and technical men, he believed, were the real benefactors of the human race because they made new things for people to *use*. How well they performed their work was determined by whether their products were a commercial success. Edison's is a harsh philosophy which still grates on many modern ears. But it was shared by most people of the United States of his time — and may still be.

The technical and administrative innovations of telephone development came from meeting expressed demands (or solving unforeseen problems) in hopes of building a working, reliable system. These complexities were not anticipated by either Bell or Watson. Research, development and innovation

103

7

have been a constant characteristic of the industry from its beginning because, without them, the growing, complex structure necessary could not survive either commercial or social test. While Vail was constructing the organization and corporate forms, he knew that it would all fail unless research continued. Throughout his two leadership periods, he continually prodded and supported his technical people and rushed their advances into full application as soon as they appeared. Even the prudent and cautious managers of his twenty-year interregnum had no choice but to prosecute vigorously the search for technical solutions that expansion demanded. The business was basically a *customer-driven* or user enterprise. Customer requirements drove the engineers unmercifully and sometimes to exhaustion.

The first switchboard was used to connect phones between doctors and drug stores. It was installed at Hartford, Connecticut in July, 1877. Hard-drawn copper wire replaced the noisy and unreliable iron of telegraph days. It was strong enough to be hung on poles and was produced in 1878 by the Ansonia Brass Company at the urging of Thomas Doolittle, the Bridgeport exchange holder of Bell's license. The same year Doolittle also introduced the pay phone in public places.

According to Watson, the most intractable problem was the mingling of conversations due to electrical interference, called "crosstalk." Early lines consisted of one wire, returning the circuit through the ground, as in telegraph practice. Until two wires twisted together to eliminate foreign voltages were made universal for every phone a few years later, this problem was never satisfactorily solved.

Watson retired from his exhausting labors in 1881, at the age of 27, "to begin his education," he said, but his work was carried on by Berliner and several other inventing minds he had gathered to succeed him. This group was the spearhead for the technical assault and, forty years later, evolved into Bell Telephone Laboratories.

In 1884, commercial service between Boston and New York, using the new copper wire, cost two dollars for five minutes in daytime, one dollar at night. Philadelphia-New York came in 1885, Chicago in 1892. Each advance in extending transmission distances triggered immediate application throughout the country to connect communities with mutual interests. Until the invention and development of the vacuum tube, the absolute limit for an unamplified telephone call, using every technique at its boundary, was from New York to Denver. This occurred in 1911. The electronic age which followed was accelerated by the rush of backlog problems demanding solution which had to wait for the breakthrough.

American Industrial Growth:

Industry	1865	1900
Coal	12,000,000 tons	212,000,000 tons
Oil	9,000 barrels	64,000 barrels
Steel	20,000 tons	10,000,000 tons

Bell engineers' names dominate the flood of electronic inventions which burst on the world following De Forest's invention of the three-element tube in 1906. Marconi's transatlantic radio signal of 1901 had been detected by a "coherer" — a glass tube of iron filings which "cohered" when a radio wave was received. The vacuum tube thus brought together telephone and radio technology. Bell scientists played an important part in both fields, as we shall see.

Artist's conception of the world's first commercial telephone exchange opened in New Haven, January 28, 1878.

The first switchboard in New Haven, 1878. It had eight telephone lines connecting 21 subscribers.

LIST OF SUBSCRIBERS.

New Haven District Telephone Company.

OFFICE 219 CHAPEL STREET.

February 21, 1878.

Residence.
Rev. JOHN E. TODD.
J. B. CARRINGTON.
H. B. BIGELOW.
C. W. SCRANTON.
GEORGE W. COY.
G. L. FERRIS.
H. P. FROST.
I. H. BROMLEY.
M. F. TYLER.
GEO. E. THOMPSON.
WALTER LEWIS.

Physicians.
DR. E. L. R. THOMPSON.
DR. A. E. WINCHELL.
DR. C. S. THOMSON, Fair Haven.

Dentists.
DR. E. S. GAYLORD.
DR. R. F. BURWELL.

Miscellaneous.
REGISTER PUBLISHING CO.
POLICE OFFICE.
POST OFFICE.
MERCANTILE CLUB.
QUINNIPIAC CLUB.
F. V. McDONALD, Yale News.
SMEDLEY BROS. & CO.
M. F. TYLER, Law Chambers.

Stores, Factories, &c.
O. A. DORMAN.
STONE & CHIDSEY.
NEW HAVEN FLOUR CO. State St.
" " " Cong. ave.
" " " Grand St.
" " " Fair Haven.
ENGLISH & MERSICK.
New Haven FOLDING CHAIR CO.
H. HOOKER & CO.
W. A. ENSIGN & SON.
H. B. BIGELOW & CO.
C. COWLES & CO.
C. S. MERSICK & CO.
SPENCER & MATTHEWS.
PAUL ROESSLER.
E. S. WHEELER & CO.
ROLLING MILL CO.
APOTHECARIES HALL.
E. A. GESSNER.
AMERICAN TEA CO.

Meat and Fish Markets.
W. H. HITCHINGS, City Market.
GEO. E. LUM.
A. FOOTE & CO.
STRONG, HART & CO.

Hack and Boarding Stables.
CRUTTENDEN & CARTER.
BARKER & RANSOM.

Office open from 6 A. M. to 2 A. M.
After March 1st, this Office will be open all night.

First telephone directory.

A Station Set for Western Electric Automatic Systems, ca. 1904.

Guglielmo Marconi in 1896. He took the experiments of Hertz and other scientists and developed them into a method of sending wireless telegraph messages. In 1901, he sent the first signals across the Atlantic.

7

The task of switching all lines to connect any one with any other is simple when a few are involved and staggering when there are many. (The number of possibilities to be handled is roughly equal to one-half the number of phones times the total number of phones, e.g., for ten phones, you need fifty switches; for a thousand, 500 thousand switches; and so on, the switches growing immensely in proportion to each new customer added.) All of the exchanges and offices had to be tied together in some grand design: thousands of inventions were necessary to realize that design.

One example of the origin of something we all take for granted illustrates how subtle social change depends on both a technical problem and the accidents of human affairs. The early exchanges listed only the names of "subscribers" to the service, and the operators had to memorize all of them in order to connect one to the other. The sensible idea of a telephone *number* was vigorously resisted by customers as an indignity and loss of personal identification. However, in 1880 at Lowell, Massachusetts, a respected physician, Dr. Parker, during an epidemic of measles recommended the use of *numbers* because he feared paralysis of the town's telephone system if the four operators succumbed. He felt that substitute operators could be trained more easily if an emergency disabled experienced personnel. When introduced, the practicality of the arrangement was quickly perceived and became general. In 1895, official instructions to operators specified "Number, please?" as the proper response to a customer.

Calls to fire departments, police, doctors, and hospitals handled by the Bell System have saved more lives in 100 years than any invention in human history. Over 6 million calls were made in 1975 in New York City requesting police, fire, and ambulance services.

Incidentally, the early operators in the United States were young boys, but their language and high jinks soon showed their unsuitability. In September 1878, Emma M. Nutt, a former telegraph operator, was hired as the first woman telephone operator, beginning a long-service tradition. She retired in 1915. In France, women operators were employed from the start, because all boys and young men were compelled to serve in the armed forces.

The evolution of the Bell System can be seen as the interactive working-out of *two* systems — the human beings involved and the mechanical and electrical apparatus used in their jobs. Each has been — and still is — influenced by the requirements and limitations of the other. Even in the early years, the mushrooming growth of the switching problem — done entirely by operators — showed the need to augment the human effort with mechanized equipment.

The first patent for an "automatic" switcher was granted in 1891 to a Kansas City undertaker, Almon Strowger, who, legend has it, felt that operators were purposely harassing him by giving his customers false "busy" signals and wrong numbers to drive him out of business. Frustrated, he vented his aggression by building a switcher which required no operators. His first model, constructed of pins and bits of metal in a collar-box, was limited to 99 numbers and required a very strong battery. Customers had to push buttons in strict and precise sequence. Five wires connected each phone to the exchange. It actually worked. The first system was installed in La Porte, Indiana in 1892 by the Automatic Electric Company, which was formed to exploit the patent. The familiar dial replaced the buttons in 1896, when Milwaukee's city hall was

Emma M. Nutt, the first female employee of the Bell System, hired on September 1, 1878 at the Boston exchange. She retired in 1915.

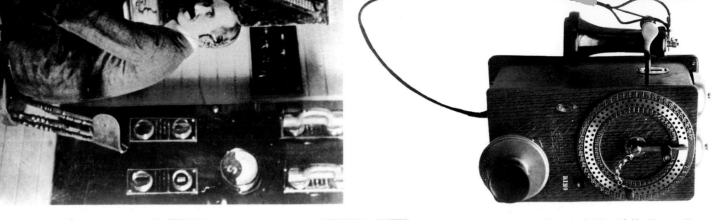

served by Automatic Electric.

Vail's grand design of a communications system equal to the nation's needs required an absolutely dependable source for all apparatus and equipment. Much of it was new, the result of basic inventions or novel demands, often employing complex, precise components which had to function under heavy loads without breakdown. At first, Charles Williams' shop — where Watson did his work — furnished the instruments, but the demand was too great. Supplies were then secured from a variety of factories with unsatisfactory results.

Meantime, Western Union built a manufacturing company from Elisha Gray's original shop to produce its own equipment. In 1881, the American Bell Telephone Company purchased Jay Gould's interest in the manufacturing company. With its name changed to Western Electric, and the transfer of the telephone patents from Williams' shop which it absorbed,

the company became the sole supplier of equipment to the Bell operations. Its engineering department worked in close cooperation with both the research people at the parent company and the local companies who used the equipment.

This integration of invention, development, manufacture and use was essential to match the pace of demand the entire industry was experiencing. Since then, Western Electric has become the purchasing and distributing arm for all components of the Bell operations, and also carries on the quality assurance, repair and salvage work associated with equipment it originally made and sold. It also installs, to local company specifications, the complex switching and transmission facilities required for their job of customer service. And it deals with 40,000 separate firms in buying the array of things needed for the constant maintenance and enhancement of today's system.

Thus the coherent forces to realize the grand design were

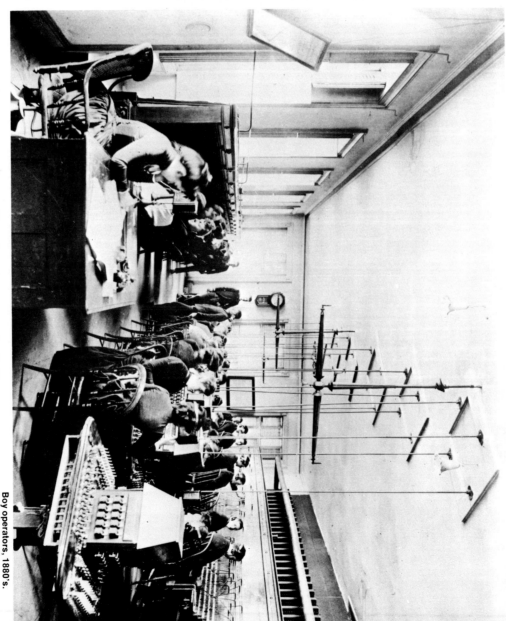

Boy operators, 1880's.

A 1900 Common Battery. The first telephones were voice-powered. Then wet batteries were used with fluids occasionally leaking on floors; and then, finally, dry batteries were installed. In 1900, however, a "common battery" device was introduced, telephones receiving power from central exchanges. There were now over 5 million calls a day coming from Bell telephones.

7

rapidly, but surely, assembled and deployed for action. Like a gigantic orchestra, each was skilled in a specific instrument and indispensable function. But all played from the same score.

Looming over these labors, like a ticking time-bomb, was a completely predictable event: the end of the seventeen years which marks the life of a patent. Bell's two patents would expire in 1893 and 1894 and the protection and encouragement a patent conferred would cease. After that, anyone could use them for any purpose whatever, at no cost or liability to himself. The overgenerous dividend policy of the Boston financiers — which had caused Vail to leave — made the telephone business look like a money machine. Many persons, eager for a piece of such a business, waited impatiently for the start of the gold rush when Bell's invention would enter the public domain. There were many areas without service, despite the frenzied pace of construction, and the charges were relatively high, about $100 a year for a residence, $150 for a business phone. In 1892, there were 240,000 phones in service. The demand continued to swamp supply, even in the large cities. It was an opportunity for anyone who could throw together a company, cut prices to get initial business from the Bell people and, hopefully, rake in profits. Or so it seemed.

"Whatever is not nailed down is mine. Whatever I can pry loose is not nailed down." C. P. Huntington (19th century American "Robber Baron")

In the six years following the patent expiration, six-thousand companies were established throughout the country, each "independent" of the older firm. Competition for customers and territory produced confusion. The uncoordinated "every man for himself" attitude led to erosion of service standards. Duplication of facilities caused unnecessary public inconvenience. Telephone bonanzas often produced bankruptcies as prices were optimistically cut below real costs. Solutions to the technical problems of linking all of these enterprises into a single communications system were postponed because there was no unifying vision or purpose shared by all involved. Chaos reigned.

By 1897, the symptoms of disorder were sufficiently obvious to responsible elements in the "independent" movement. They formed the United States Independent Telephone Association in Detroit to attack mutual problems then hampering their progress. The organization exists today and, while the early years of Bell-Independent relations were marked by fierce competition and bitter controversy which benefitted no one, now both entities cooperate in technical and administrative matters to serve the entire nation under modern conditions.

Meanwhile, the Bell organization was coping with the confusing problems of success. Improved technology was urgently needed. Funds to finance expansion were called for in constantly increasing amounts far beyond the capability of internal sources. The task of continuing the momentum of progress was awesome. Debt securities soared as few investors were attracted to permanent ownership in an industry so beset with uncertainty and risk. The Bell Company was forced to expand through borrowing, trusting, like Charles Dickens' character, Mr. Micawber, that "something would turn up" to make things right.

In 1900, company officials called on Vail to return. He refused to leave his making and losing fortunes in organizing municipal heating and street railways in various countries, give up extensive international tours or abandon the enjoyment of

Bell at the New York end of the circuit to Chicago in 1892. The line was opened as part of the ceremonies beginning the Chicago Columbian Exposition.

108

The Spanish-American War saw the first war-time role played by the telephone. These phones were installed by the U.S. Army Signal Corps.

1890's telephone men promoting 5¢ a day service.

San Francisco Traffic Operator, China Exchange, 1895. This was the first switchboard handled by one person.

life on his estate in the Vermont hills. After Vail's rejection, a distinguished patent lawyer, Frederick Fish, accepted the presidency, unwillingly. His interests and skills lay in protection and defense against the independents rather than gearing a business to public consent and expectation. Nevertheless, he inaugurated a massive expansion and building program whose finance saturated the market for telephone securities. By 1907, the absence of investor interest and a general panic in the capital markets created a crisis for the now massive enterprise. Fish had indeed put vigor into the business and restored its growth again. But the effort broke him, and he wished to retire. Now, some great stroke was needed both to restore confidence and secure the understanding of the customers, employees and stockholders.

The bankers recommended making Vail president and bringing the headquarters to New York. The offer found Vail ready. Depressed over the recent death of his wife and son;

Speedwell Farms.

Vail's yacht.

satisfied with his work in South America, now successfully completed; and unchallenged by the insufficient use of his physical and mental energies in his life as a country squire, he considered politics. But the methods of that art repelled him. Five years before, a fortune teller in Paris prophesied that his greatest work would be done after his sixtieth year. This was confirmed by another reading in London. Both were right. He was 62. His mere appearance at the meeting of company officials with the investigating committee established by the bankers created a sensation and surge of confidence. After taking the officials to his farm for long discussions about the company's affairs, he told his sister he had decided to accept. To her objections he replied, "No, I must take it. It is the crowning thing of my life. I refused it six years ago; I am in a position to take it now. Besides, now they need me."

It was an understatement.

"Vision is the art of seeing things invisible." *Jonathan Swift* (1706)

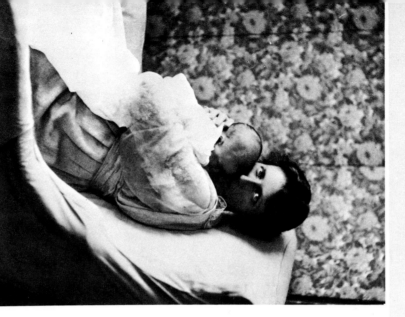

First Christmas at the small house, Vermont.

Vail and a "sugaring-off" party at the Vermont farm.

Vail's niece, Katherine Vail Marsters and daughter.

Vail and grandchild.

A pastoral scene at Speedwell Farms with the now common presence of telephone poles.

A niece's horse being shown at the Vermont State Fair (1900's).

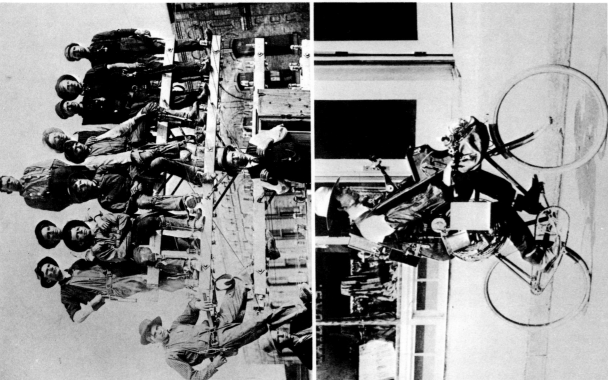

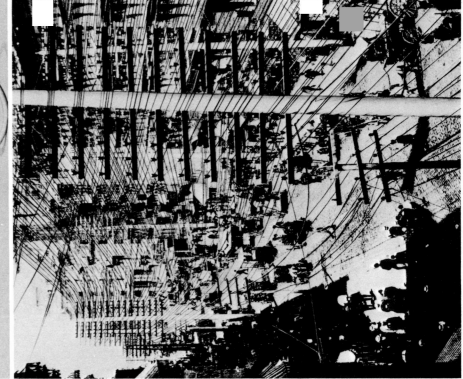

Left column, top to bottom:

A Beltz post-hole digger a year before the completion of the transcontinental line. Nevada, 1914. The Indian village looks much the same as it did 100 years before.

Pole setting line crew in central Pennsylvania, 1900.

Small Wisconsin town and the new presence of the telephone.

Right column, top to bottom:

A safety-man's nightmare — Canadian telephone men celebrate the completion of a pole line in the 1890's. Their victory consisted of them climbing atop the tallest pole.

1911 vintage "Complete Telephone Man", mobile, well-equipped, mechanized. He carried with him all the elements needed to install a miracle of communications.

The growth of overhead telephone wires. New York City's Broadway in the 1880's. There are about 350 wires visible.

CHAPTER

8

8

THE LATE-BLOOMING OF WATSON: EXCURSIONS AND EXPLORATIONS

One of the important concerns of our time is how to stimulate economic development and useful social change. This is a problem for both "developed" and "developing" nations. The subject is covered with an immense literature but curiously neglects the essential role of talented individuals. Initiative and human spirit seem either taken for granted or dismissed as unimportant. Yet progressive minds, fueled by enthusiasm and dreams, are the tiny spores of social fermentation. Wheat needs yeast to make bread: such minds are just as essential to transform latent resources into human accomplishments. This is a mysterious process and such people seem driven by strange, occult forces. No satisfactory general theory exists to explain their apparently erratic behavior, but their individual lives tell us something of both their indispensability to social processes and the conditions which nurture them.

The subsequent careers of Bell and Watson show how the efforts of their success in one domain, the telephone, rippled into other diverse fields of human endeavor. Their lives affirm the explorer's view of life that "as one door closes, another opens."

THE IMPACT OF EUROPE: Still very young on retirement from his telephone labors, Watson felt himself raw and un-educated. The elegant Bell taught him the table manners of a gentleman as they consumed Watson's lunches wrapped in brown paper. Bell showed him the delights of music, literature, drama and science. And Bell knew that Watson possessed an untapped mine of assets: curiosity, stamina, an adventurous disposition, adaptability, alertness, and, most importantly, an open-mindedness to any new knowledge and its potential application. Eventually, Watson would use them all.

A month after leaving the business, Watson sailed for Liverpool on an old ship, the *Batavia*. The ascetic regimen of seasickness during two weeks of North Atlantic gales turned his mind into the philosophic channels it was never to leave, even during the most hectic periods of later ventures. "If I had been exposed to a higher education which would have lasted until well in my twenties," he wrote, "my appetite for study would have been satisfied and I should have been contented to stick to one job all my life, but my early schooling, limited as it was in amount and poor in quality, had done for me the best thing any school can do for a boy. It turned me out with an insatiable desire to know more." This first trip to Europe supported that desire.

Consider his itinerary. After a few days inspecting Liverpool, he went off to London acquiring a taste for churches, palaces, museums, historical buildings, Dickens' localities and picture galleries. But sightseeing was no substitute for work. After two weeks, he went off to Norway to visit one of his old assistants and to see something of fjords, mountains and family life. All his life, he retained a preference for living with families when on tour rather than staying at a hotel. After Copenhagen, he settled in Hanover staying for two months, learning German, beginning to read Goethe, Schiller and Heine. Music pervaded much of German social life and Watson became enamoured of it. He traveled up the Rhine to Switzerland and on to Paris spending two months in an attic "suite." Here he learned French, studied history and literature, attended the theater and took fencing lessons.

Watson in 1881.

117

"O this learning! what a thing it is." *Taming of the Shrew.*

Meeting Bell at the Exposition then underway, he accompanied the Prince of Wales (later Edward VII) who was touring the electrical exhibits, and found that his own interest in

London slums of the 19th century as depicted by Gustav Doré.

Late 19th century London outside the Houses of Parliament.

electrical matters had been satisfied. A visit to a French machine shop rekindled the itch for contact with tools and machinery, and he did some consulting work for the promoters of the French telephone company. During December, he fled bad weather and visited Lyons, Arles, Avignon and Marseilles on

118

Paris Exposition, 1878.

his way to the Riviera, winning his expenses at Monte Carlo. Then he went on to Florence, Genoa, Pisa and Rome where he settled down for the winter, learning Italian and serving as a guide to tourists of the historical and cultural sights. In the spring, Naples, Venice, Geneva, and Paris once again claimed him. He discovered an interest in geology. Returning to London, he was met by a subpoena for testimony in the English telephone patent suits. Before he left for the United States after his year abroad, he estimated that the entire trip had been more than paid for by his fees as an expert and the proceeds of his own foreign patent licenses. Not a bad beginning for a life-long education, which laid the foundation for his later achievements. After spending what remained of the summer in studying music, Latin and mathematics, building a house for his sister and selling the rest of his foreign patents, he married Elizabeth Kimball and they went to California for their honeymoon.

Since he always wanted to try farming, he returned East and bought a farm on the Fore River at East Braintree, Massachusetts. The location *alone* influenced the future course of his life, as everything in his life did. After stocking the farm with every kind of machinery, he found that his laborers scorned all modern methods — and that they were right! Leaving the farming to his hired hands, Watson spent more and more time in the machine shop he had fitted up in a barn. Soon he became involved with developing a rotary steam engine (a failure). He hired Frank Wellington, a young machinist, and together they developed and built a steam engine for yachts and tug boats, which became the best of its kind. Soon orders poured in for both that model and larger engines. He expanded the shops to the river edge, now employing thirty men. Bookkeeping claimed his attention, and he constructed a card system, which was extremely fast and accurate. It had most of the features of today's computer systems. He used the system for all subsequent projects. It was a remarkable conceptual breakthrough which he executed almost casually.

At this time he became a member of the Athenaeum, Boston's intellectual club. He promptly devoured its library.

As the engine shop prospered, he took elocution lessons, continuing the abiding interest in the practice of public speaking sparked by Bell. He and his wife began a serious study of geology at the Lowell Institute. Graduating after two years, they entered the Massachusetts Institute of Technology as students in geology, paleontology and other related sciences. His contributions to geology were highly esteemed by professionals, and a *genus* of Cambrian fossils, "Watsonella," was named for him.

PUBLIC THINGS: In 1890, Watson set up a "People's Institute" in a local church to encourage others in pursuit of the self-education he so prized. He also established a kindergarten for his own children and those of his neighbors and workmen. Its success led others to copy the idea throughout the state.

Appointed as head of a commission on school building, he not only designed and built new schools but also undertook

the remodeling of all existing ones, making the town's overall system a model which was widely copied and which led to his chairmanship of the school board for many years.

Converted to the utopian programs of Edward Bellamy, Watson became a leader in the then current "nationalist" movement for cooperative and public ownership. He subsidized their weekly paper and organized a municipally owned electric company. His experiences with government inefficiency as manager of the electric company led him to conclude that "I am still interested in socialism as a philosophy, but before it can be successfully put into practice I fancy the forces of evolution must work an age or two longer on the spirit of man." His public association with Bellamy's ideas gained him the reputation of a radical. Invitations came from time to time to enter state or national politics, but his Populism was an impediment.

"When the poor have cried, Caesar hath wept; Ambition should be made of sterner stuff." *Julius Caesar, 2*

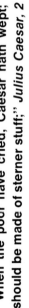

Watson's Braintree, Massachusetts home, 1890's.

Machine Shop, Fore River shipyard ca. 1900.

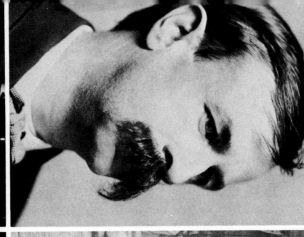

Edward Bellamy.

Watson in his library.

Boston in the 1880's.

Unemployed, ca. 1900's.

THE SHIPBUILDER: The Great Depression in the 1890s caused much unemployment in his area, where the primary business was shoemaking. To keep his own men working, Watson had branched out into making boat hulls, printing presses and shoe machinery. But orders for these items soon succumbed to the depression. However, when the country awoke to the need for building up its Navy, Congress appropriated funds for several torpedo boat destroyers, vessels never before built in the United States. Watson, desperate at the plight of the town, promptly drew up plans for the warships, sent in his bid to Washington, and, in a few months, was awarded the contract for two ships. He simultaneously designed a steam automobile in case the ships were rejected, but abandoned that on news of the naval acceptance. He had to build a shipyard and assemble its tools and machinery. Initially, he did so with his own funds, but Boston financiers assured him that bonds and stock could be raised when needed. The surge of activity wiped out unemployment for miles around, and from this slender, courageous beginning a great shipbuilding industry grew, which was to be a major factor for years in the economy of the region. (In time it would bankrupt Watson.) Successfully coping with the unique and demanding technical standards of warships called for constant infusions of money — his own funds and the government payment in-

Watson in 1890.

The *Lawrence.*

stallments all going immediately to the men and supplies. He felt later that he would have fared better had he simply given everyone in the area a pension!

As the destroyers moved along, he had to find other work to keep all the operations busy. Over the next few years these are some of the things his staff built: a battle cruiser, the *Des Moines;* the largest shipyard in the United States, at Quincy; a railroad to serve it; the great "lightship," *Cape Hatteras;* a large drawbridge erected by novel methods; two battleships, the *Rhode Island* and *New Jersey;* a seven-masted schooner for the coal trade, the largest ever built; a five-masted schooner; steel barges for floating railroad cars in New York; two river liners — and all carried out with his own capital *which he obtained by selling all his telephone stock and other securities.* He said he never had a business, merely "lived in an epic poem." The financial pressures were so great that his treasurer collapsed and died. During World War I, at its peak operations, the yard turned out most of the submarines as well as a wide range of large vessels used by the Navy.

Watson's little exercise in relieving unemployment put twenty-thousand men to work. But the bankers who promised the new capital demanded as well a new president, and Watson stepped aside to keep the yard going. Thus, in 1903, the Fore River Ship and Engine Company, begun twenty-two years

1880 Blake transmitter adapted in a primitive desk set. Francis Blake Jr. adapted a carbon transmitter (based on original work by Thomas A. Edison) and greatly improved voice clarity.

American war ships defeating the Spanish fleet in Battle of Manila Bay, May, 1898.

Des Moines

Launching of the Diamond Shoals Light Ship.

Seven-masted schooner, *Thomas W. Lawson*, built in 1902, lost in a storm in the English Channel, December 15, 1907.

before in his barn, passed from Watson's hands. He lost his entire investment in it, part of the price for its continued existence. But Watson, devoid of rancor, remained proud of its contributions to defense until he died. Characteristically, he said that only his beloved geology and the works of Whitman, Browning and Emerson carried him through these years. He began each day with a half-hour reading "from their inspired minds," to clear his vision and calm his mind.

REJUVENATION: After a shock that might have destroyed other men, Watson returned to his rocks and other studies, experiencing a freedom previously unknown. Reduced to living on the proceeds of a small trust fund he had set up for his family's protection, he augmented his income by public readings of plays and poetry, a vocation he continued for many years. He also formed a partnership with his old professor of geology, and they became experts in assessing prospective mines. Rugged trips from the mountains and islands of Alaska

to Death Valley, California rebuilt his health and greatly raised his spirits. He was particularly knowledgeable on methods used to defraud naive investors in new mining property, and *his* clients were never bilked by charlatans. He developed lectures on these travels and found a steady demand for them.

Another advanced idea, radical even for our own era, called for a plan to harmonize the interests of labor, capital and consumers by giving representation on boards of directors to employees and the general public. He turned this scheme into a lecture, and printed a pamphlet that was well received in 1907, but the idea has been tried only in Europe during the second half of this century. Restored to work but rejecting many business offers, he took on more lectures and began the serious study of music and painting.

"They mocked thee for too much curiosity."
Timon of Athens

THE ACTOR: By 1910, his extensive lecturing triggered an

Building the Panama Canal (1904-1914). The American victory over Spain pressed the need for a two-ocean Navy. The Canal was one of the great engineering feats in history and made the United States a world power.

urge to improve "the most subtle of all arts, that of human speech." Watson heard of Frank Benson's Shakespearean Company which had toured large English cities for 25 years and took a few young men and women students as apprentices each season. Many leading English actors trained in its ranks. Benson accepted Watson's application with a note ending, "If you are not risking your all in joining us, you will be welcomed and will, I am sure, find the work interesting and beneficial." Benson was right. Watson recalled it as the most delightful year of his life — begun when he was 56.

Arriving in London, he enrolled his wife in university courses and, after signing on, was given a third-class rail ticket for Bath with instructions to report to the Theatre Royal. Living on tour in seedy, but congenial, theatrical boarding houses, he applied himself with gusto to constant rehearsals and performances of an astonishing range of plays. He was part

Watson as a Lord in *Much Ado About Nothing,* Stratford, May, 1911. "He hath borne himself beyond the promise of his age."

of "the crowd" in *The Pied Piper,* and played sundry peasants, soldiers, priests and burghers in *A Winter's Tale, The Taming of the Shrew, Twelfth Night,* and *The Merchant of Venice.* Benson gave arduous instruction in classes held every day, including elocution, calisthenics, stage gestures, falling, fencing and dancing. Watson loved it all and regretted that American child labor laws kept young children from taking up the exhilarating profession. In every town Watson used Baedeker's guides and a geological atlas to investigate the areas as well as become acquainted with the local populations and their various ways of life.

In Birmingham, the company added *Macbeth, The Merry Wives of Windsor* and *Julius Caesar* to the repertoire, and he commanded an "army" on stage. To Watson's delight, each performance had its memorable moments and hilarious events. The twelve-week tour covered Liverpool, Bradford, Manches-

Watson as a Priest in *Midsummer Night's Dream,* Stratford, May, 1911.

◁Watson as the Clerk in *Merchant of Venice,* Stratford, May, 1911. "How far that little candle throws his beams! So shines a good deed in a naughty world."

1886 Long Distance Transmitter. The search △ for improved methods of transmitting speech led to the development of this model which used a platinum diaphragm for better long distance transmission. The instrument shown in this picture actually was used by Bell and later by Theodore N. Vail.

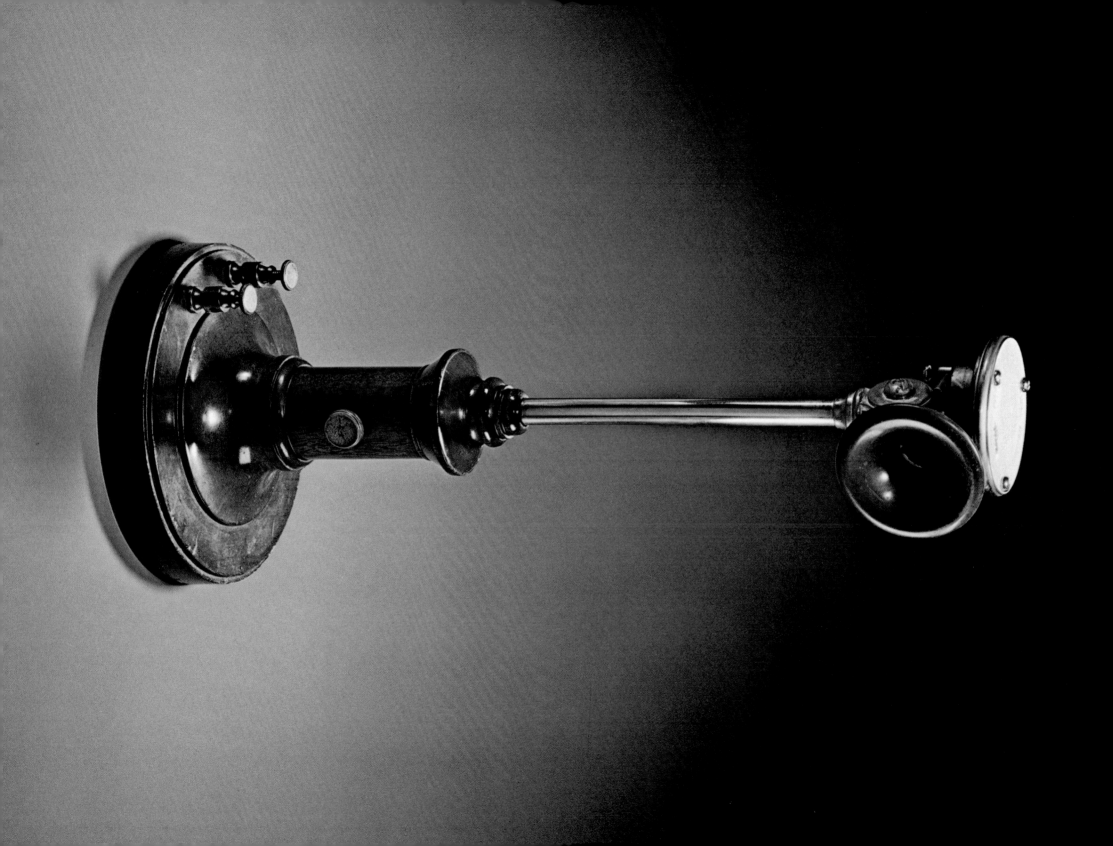

ter, as well as many towns in between, and added a five-week London season. After that success, the tour to Scotland and the North began, adding *Hamlet, King John, Henry V* and *Much Ado About Nothing* to the list. Watson was advanced to speaking parts in all the plays and did splendidly.

"Out of my lean and low ability, I'll lend you something."
Twelfth Night

The actors, fearing no work at the tour's end, organized a company to play at the resorts and smaller towns during the summer. Watson was invited to join, promised leading roles, and accepted. However, the manager could not get the rights to all the plays he wanted and asked Watson, by now a seasoned trouper, to write some, suggesting Dickens' novels as appropriate source material as it was the centenary year of the great writer's birth. Though he had never written a line of drama, Watson wrote three plays during the last weeks on the road. Their titles were *A Tale of Two Cities, Oliver Twist* and *Nicholas Nickleby*. The climax of the Benson tour was at Stratford where

Sarah Bernhardt (1844-1923) as Hamlet. The finest actress of her day, a contemporary of Watson's.

1897 Desk Set, made of cast bronze, was a refinement of previous models.

they added *Midsummer Night's Dream, Othello, Richard III, As You Like It,* and *Romeo and Juliet* to their already extensive offerings. Leading actors from London joined the month-long festival. Now Watson believed that he had at last experienced the heights of the speaking arts. He treasured Benson's farewell: "Don't lose your eternal youth, Mr. Watson."

Two weeks later, the improvised company, with Watson playing important roles, began their assault on the southern resort towns, with a collapsing guillotine, shaky scenery, actors mixing up Watson's lines from three plays into one, and costumes indiscriminately jumbled. After the gloom and hysterics were absorbed and original deficits covered by Watson, the company enjoyed great success. His daughter came over from Radcliffe to play both small parts and classical piano interludes. She was often approached by sympathetic old ladies who said what a shame it was that so fine a pianist had to be in such disreputable company and offered to help her get respectable work.

Watson learned a great deal from theater people whose "courage, kindness, patience and endurance" profoundly impressed him. This was his second attempt to furnish employment to deserving persons. It produced one of the high points of his life. Characteristically, Watson gave his plays and his entire investment as a gift to the players. Had he been younger, he would have made acting his profession.

ANCIENT ROOTS: The Watsons now set off for Egypt, via Münich, Salzburg, the Alps and Trieste. He conducted geological inspections and collected fossils in the Valley of the Kings during an extended trip up the Nile. Typically, he soon gave public lectures in Luxor, complete with exhibits. Bothered by hordes of people eager to sell their goods and services, he found a simple way to be left alone. Sensing the important place of religion in their lives, he would simply say quietly to a pressing, chattering crowd, "Go away; I want to pray," and

Pyramids.

1910 Desk Set. This somewhat streamlined pedestal desk telephone first appeared in black finish in 1910 though its nickel plated prototype dates back to the turn of the century. These telephones were made of cast brass and later steel and were the all-American standard for the next quarter century. Some still are in use.

secured complete solitude. Returning by way of Sicily, Italy and France, the Watsons reached home in 1912. The two years abroad furnished training and material he would use the rest of his life.

END GAMES: Watson soon used his new skills to give public readings from the Bible, Greek drama, Shakespeare, Browning, Whitman and the best current plays and poems. He brought new vigor and professionalism to amateur theatricals in Boston, made plays from Browning's works and played many leading parts. He also delivered addresses discussing his travels and geological investigations. His most popular lecture was delivered in 1913 to the first meeting of the Telephone Pioneers — veterans who had served the business more than 21 years — entitled *The Birth and Babyhood of the Telephone*. He gave the talk for many years thereafter and a pamphlet version is still in demand.

His last official involvement with the telephone occurred on the inauguration of the first transcontinental telephone line in 1915. From San Francisco, Watson talked to Bell in New York, President Woodrow Wilson in Washington and Theodore Vail in Georgia. At one point, Bell connected a replica of Watson's first phone to the line and said, "Mr. Watson, come here, I want you." Watson replied that he would be glad to come, but it would now take a week instead of a minute. Thus he dramatized the vast differences in speed that had occurred between transmission of information and transportation. He was the last survivor of that original band who brought the telephone into existence and made it a social force. Returning to his base cabin in the Colorado mountains — still fascinated by massive peaks since first seeing them during experiments with Bell — he received word of Bell's death in 1922.

Mr. and Mrs. Watson viewing the evolution of the telephone in a Pennsylvania exhibit, 1920's.

1928 Desk Set. A new telephone look for the Roaring Twenties based on European designs. The combined receiver-transmitter idea, used by linemen since 1878, was now improved for general services. It was nick-named "the French phone."

"That what he will, he does; and does so much,
That proof is call'd impossibility."
            Troilus and Cressida

Honorary degrees, medals, fellowships and citations flowed to Watson during his later years. But he continued his cultural studies with the same old energies until his death in Florida in 1934. Because he had lived, the world was a different place. The telephone catapulted him into domains unknown to the boy of Salem, and he left his mark on each.

SIGNIFICANCE: In our age, where mere schooling is too often equated with real education, Watson's development shows the tremendous powers and possibilities of self-education — something we are in danger of forgetting. But it also shows the kind of environment needed for it to flower. Opportunity, example, recognition, books, work, leisure and

A Watson Family Album.

His final role: Watson with group making a film for the Bell System.

Watson re-enacting the great discovery, early 1930's.

Watson continuing the explorations of his remarkable curiosity.

Mr. and Mrs. Watson.

Mr. and Mrs. Watson at the Museum of the New York Telephone Company.

Watson and friends at his Massachusetts home, 1930's.

Radio, the newest miracle.

Watson holding gallows model after receiving an honorary degree from Amherst College, Massachusetts.

Mr. and Mrs. Watson at their Florida home.

liberty are all essential. The America of those days was well endowed with every one of these requisites, and the task of any society which aims at bringing forth the latent powers of its citizens is to increase these aspects of a good society. Watson's was only one life, but it was one which reminds us of timeless truths needed for any human progress worthy of the name.

The telephone developed as it did because the cultural environment elicited and encouraged the talents of people like Watson; and its growth in turn affected, in profound ways, the course of the human environment which gave it birth.

"Then shall our names,
Familiar in their mouths as household words —
Be in their flowing cups freshly remembered."

Henry V

Watson at creative work, 1934.

CHAPTER

9

6

BELL'S HARVEST OF EMINENCE: CURIOSITY UNBOUND

While it is relatively easy to trace the course of an invention's primary impact on society; those effects caused by the *inventor* himself are unique and so unpredictable as to appear almost random. Hyperactive personalities produce events and discontinuities bringing to human affairs both the hope of progress and the terrors of uncertainty. Few men so illustrate this phenomenon as well as Alexander Graham Bell.

From wide recognition which sent him rocketing to fame at the age of thirty, Bell's interests and energy made him a powerful force in developing a remarkable variety of fields, because he had an astonishing ability to awake public interest in scientific and social investigations. A human being full of quirks, talents, foibles and faults, his battle against the deadening weight of early fame shows an unusual form of heroism. He was determined to make continuous contributions, expressing his ego in the medium of his works. Through him, the invention of the telephone transmitted waves of innovation to endeavors seemingly remote from it — but of such great importance to our evolution and environment that, like the telephone, we now take them for granted.

The rich texture of Bell's post-telephone activities form meaningful patterns which criss-cross each other throughout the chronicle. His major interests included: a constant preoccupation with education of the deaf and amelioration of their social deprivation, sponsorship of scientific pioneers, personal scientific investigations and the pursuit of new inventions, advocacy of new ideas to which his dignity and eminence brought respectability and recognition, organizing of societies and publications for the "increase and diffusion of knowl-

edge," and finally the honing of his own skills and character as tools for cutting the "cake of custom" in effecting needed reforms of his era.

FOUNDATIONS: Returning from England, Bell severed active connection with telephone affairs, with the troubling exception of patent litigation. He was paid $3,000 a year by the infant Bell Company until 1880. The rapid increase in the value of his and his wife's holdings in the company furnished the life-long financial independence on which his later work was built. Robert V. Bruce, author of Bell's definitive biography, estimated that, by 1883, at age 36, Bell was close to being a millionaire. He decided to settle in Washington, living in the house Hubbard built as base for his government relations and made a commitment to become a U.S. citizen (achieved in 1882). After living in rented quarters, he bought a great mansion in 1882 which occupied an entire block. In 1891 he built a new town house at 1331 Connecticut Avenue, near Du Pont Circle which soon became a hub for the capital's intellectual, social and scientific circles. He and Mabel lived there the rest of their lives.

Long summers were spent on Canada's Cape Breton Island at a magnificent estate which Bell built after a visit in 1885. Named *Beinn Bhreagh* (Gaelic for *Beautiful Mountain*), its vistas reminded him of his native Scotland and became the site for much of his outdoor experimentation. Bell died there and is buried on its rocky peak. The rhythm of his life was polarized between these two princely residences which symbolized both the intense involvement and withdrawal which marked his temperament.

Bell in 1876.

Bell's was a complex personality. Aloof and dignified in public, warm and patriarchal in private, he was a very formal man and used the arts of the elocutionist in all speech. *Only two people, besides his father, addressed him by his first name.* He pursued authentic scientific status his entire life, but it eluded him, in spite of his great contributions towards making science into a grand, collective effort. Minimizing technological accomplishments in commentary, he nevertheless minutely documented his own works and rushed to patent them. Giving great energy and funds for the widest dissemination of knowledge, he persisted until the end of his days in working everything out for himself, often repeating experiments already well established by others. Accepting nothing on faith, he relished attacking existing views and theories and was often saved from embarrassing publication by the kindly, private judgments of

Bell in the study of his Washington, D.C. home, 1884.

Dupont Circle, a fashionable section of Washington, D.C., shown in the 1890's.

The main house of Beinn Bhreagh in Nova ▷ Scotia.

A COMPARISON WITH EDISON: Astrologers might be interested in the fact that Edison and Bell were born within days

In 1904, after his black assistant of 35 years, Charles Thompson, was refused rooms at a Nova Scotia hotel, Bell organized a public protest in his Baddeck village and later gave a public interview in America protesting against racial discrimination.

his scientific friends. (At one time he tried to "prove" the non-existence of gravity; at another, he worked out an idea that a heavy airplane would have a better chance of flying than a light one.) Constantly complaining about lack of time, he would lavish hours and long letters on reporters, children and young experimenters. He was an accomplished pianist, enjoyed reading literature aloud to groups and participated in amateur theatricals.

of each other. Yet these two figures, whose names dominated the public mind in the field of technology, possessed characteristics which spanned the entire conceivable spectrum of what makes a successful inventor.

Bell was elegant in language; Edison earthy and coarse. Bell's pictures show that he dressed as impeccably as a diplomat; Edison was indifferent to clothing and usually slept in the plain garb of a workman's wardrobe. Edison had an inspired mechanic's hands; Bell was clumsy and always needed a young assistant to construct models and apparatus from his sketches. Bell was a family man incarnate; Edison, too preoccupied to give attention to wife or children. Edison invented things to get money for his treadmill of more inventing; Bell financed all of his work from his own funds. Bell loved society, clubs, dinners, serious conversation and the organizing of meetings; Edison loathed them all. Bell traveled everywhere; Edison preferred to remain in his shop. Bell was an imposing lecturer and prolific writer; Edison detested speechmaking and never wrote an article for publication. Bell sought the company and approbation of scientists; Edison showed contempt for them. Edison could organize large teams of engineers and scientists; Bell always preferred a tiny group of near-amateurs around him.

And they were similar in many ways. Both were deficient in mathematics, having minds of a primarily visual cast. Neither spared himself energy or time when hot on the trail of an idea or attacking a difficulty, though Bell never locked up an entire laboratory (as Edison did) refusing to let his men leave until a problem had been solved! Both were famous at early ages from inventions which caught the public's imagination and resulted in short-lived crazes for telephone and phonograph lectures. It is ironic that Edison's telephone improvement made Bell's discovery capable of wide application, and Bell's work on phonograph recording and duplication

turned Edison's invention into a popular, commercial article.

Both were active in biological studies, Edison in hybrid plants, Bell in heredity and selective breeding. Empirical in their methods, both mounted enormous numbers of experiments and trials to find materials and forms for their ideas. Omnivorous readers, their methods were haphazard, spasmodic and uninhibited in approaching the difficulty of any subject. Both were agnostics in religion. Edison was deaf, and Bell devoted much of his life to that affliction. Their powers of concentration were extraordinary, and both kept detailed, voluminous journals. But the indispensable attributes they shared were: a childlike wonder at the mysteries of creation; a stubborn, often mindless faith that diligence coupled to thought could make apparatus for penetrating those mysteries; and a purposeful serenity, devoid of all doubt, in the value of their work. Invention, admittedly, is only one species of creativity; but it is still important and needed. Its psychology remains unmapped in our time.

Thomas Alva Edison (1847-1931) at the age of 14, when he was a newsboy on the Grand Trunk Railway which ran between Port Huron and Detroit, Michigan. At the time of his death, he held over 1,300 patents.

Edison's Menlo Park Laboratory showing Edison (center, wearing cap) seated with a group of his assistants, February 20, 1880.

△ 1878 Butterstamp. Bell's first set with a combined receiver-transmitter that could be held in one hand, looked like a dairy butterstamp of the period. Designed in 1877, it was in service when the world's first switchboard opened in New Haven in 1878. The pushbutton signalled the operator.

142

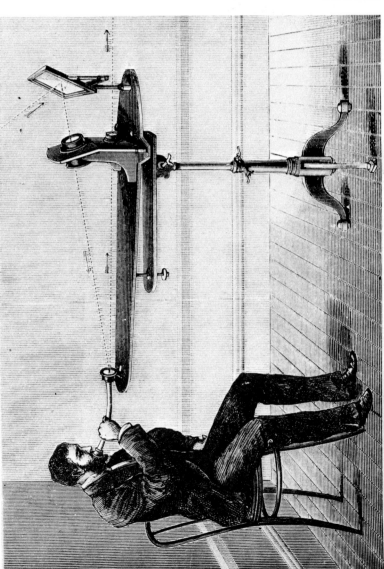

THE HIGHWAY OF INGENUITY: While in England in 1878, Bell heard of the element selenium's peculiar property of changing its electrical resistance in response to changing amounts of light impinging on it — what we now know as a photo-electric effect. His mind immediately leapt to the possibility of using the phenomenon to send messages over light beams instead of costly wires. Pursuing this prospect on his return, he hired the first of Watson's successors, Sumner

Tainter, and together they developed the photophone which *did* transmit speech via light, using a telephone-driven mirror and a selenium strip. They were granted a patent in 1880 for the device Bell considered his most profound invention. It had no permanent scientific value, and the basic idea had to await modern development of the laser beam for practical use.

In 1880, Bell became the second recipient of the Volta Prize of $10,000 established by Napoleon in honor of Alessandro

Illustration of the Photophone patented by Bell in 1880. It transmitted speech by means of reflected sunlight. "I have heard articulate speech produced by sunlight!" Bell wrote his father at the time. "I have heard a ray of the sun laugh and cough and sing! . . Can imagination picture what the future of this invention is to be!" He later said that the Photophone was "the greatest invention I have ever made; greater than the telephone."

△ Illustration of Bell using his induction apparatus to locate a bullet in President Garfield.

Volta, the Italian for whom our electrical unit, the "volt," is named. Bell always considered it his greatest honor and used the money to create a laboratory in a former stable near his home, known as the Volta Laboratory. Here, with his cousin, Chichester Bell and Tainter, he developed his subsequent electrical inventions.

Bell on his role as research group leader: "My special function . . . is the coordination of the whole — the appreciation of the importance of steps of progress — and the encouragement of efforts in what seem to me to be advancing directions."

On July 2, 1881, President Garfield was shot by an assassin, but the bullet could not be precisely located for removal. Hearing of the problem, Bell volunteered his services hoping to develop an electrical probe. His offer accepted, he organized

frenzied efforts at the Volta Laboratory, an electrical shop in Baltimore, and Johns Hopkins University, attempting to produce an "induction balance" — similar to a modern mine detector — to aid the surgeons. Several tests of apparatus conducted by Bell at the president's bedside failed, and Garfield died on September 19 from infection, not the bullet itself. Bell continued the work and produced a needle probe, using telephone techniques, which was used universally (until x-rays became common) and for which he received his honorary doctor's degree from Heidelberg University. The electric probe was extremely useful in the field surgery of World War I. The death of his son from a lung ailment stimulated Bell's invention of a machine for artificial respiration, the "vacuum jacket." It was the first version of the iron lung so beneficial in the treatment of polio.

After an initial craze, the phonograph of Edison was neglected by the public and its inventor. This was the one invention of another scientist which Bell felt he had come close to making himself. He set his Volta Laboratory associates to work on its improvement. After many explorations of alternative recording and playback methods — especially in the use of wax as a substitute for Edison's tinfoil — Bell's staff called their version the Graphophone and launched it as a commercial venture. The invention of the modern "floating stylus," patented by Tainter in 1886, was crucial. Edison, after rejecting Bell's offer to combine their work, drove his men unmercifully to eclipse the Volta Associates' improvements. The Volta patents were sold to a promoter, for which Tainter and Chichester Bell received about $100,000 each, and Bell himself $200,000. The promoter's interest was absorbed several years later by Edison who had finally made the phonograph a widespread medium of home entertainment. Bell promptly used these proceeds to establish the Volta Bureau for research

Bell with water distilling device. Moisture evaporated from salt water heated by the sun and was condensed on a sloping pane of glass. Pure distilled water trickled down the small tube into the bottle.

△

1882 Magneto Wall Set. Encased in oak, this telephone used a Blake transmitter and Bell's hand receiver. In service for many years, it was the first of the side-winder models in which the crank was turned to signal the operator, who was usually a young boy. This was the first telephone manufactured by Western Electric for the Bell System.

on problems of the deaf — the one group of persons who could not benefit from the phonograph in any other way. Tainter and Bell's cousin used their profits to finance later, independent careers of invention in California and England.

Other ideas and insights flowed from the springs of Bell's mind. He worked on sonic methods for determining ocean depths, built distilling apparatus for supplying lifeboats with fresh water, and suggested the use of radium sealed in small glass tubes for the treatment of internal cancers.

"I have become so detached from it that I often wonder if I really did invent the telephone, or was it someone else I had read about?" Bell in 1910

AERONAUTICS: Bell's interest in flight and faith in man's potential for achieving it was lifelong. Watson recalls young Alec measuring the wings of a dead sea gull on one of their walks along the beaches. And Bell, at seventy, became excited at seeing Florida buzzards leave the ground merely by facing a breeze. The years between were filled with experiments and

146

study of the ever-fascinating quest. His serious efforts resumed in 1891, after hearing the great aviation pioneer, Samuel Langley, lecture at the National Academy of Science. They were to remain close friends until death.

Bell tried and measured everything — from helicopter and

propellor blades to a bewildering variety of wings — until, in 1898, he began the building of kites to study lift and drag. The flying of these kites, some small, others the size of large rooms, was a constant source of communal life at Cape Breton and, beginning as an experimental method, soon became an obses-

148

Bell, on extreme right, watches multi-cell kite; about 1905.

The *Red Wing*. The first airplane to use treated fabric as a wing cover.

sion which never left him. Kites led Bell to his discovery of the tetrahedron — or three-sided pyramid — as the ideal "space frame" for construction of airplanes, towers and building beams. He was granted a patent for the idea in 1904, and its basic insights are applied in many of today's structures. By 1907, the work on kites and structures led Bell to form the Aerial Experiment Association, financed by Mabel, to extend their work in the direction of motorizing his large kites. Glenn Curtiss, later one of aviation's great industrialists, and Thomas Selfridge, the first Army flyer (and first man to die in an airplane accident), were two of the five-man group, with Bell as chairman. The association built four airplanes in 1908. One, the *Red Wing*, made the first American public flight at Hammondsport, New York. (The Wright Brothers had done their

work secretly in North Carolina.) Another plane of the group, *June Bug*, flown by Curtiss, won the *Scientific American* prize for the first flight of one kilometer.

Bell in 1896: "I believe that it will be possible in a very few years for a person to take his dinner in New York at 7 or 8 o'clock in the evening and eat his breakfast in either Ireland or England the following morning."

The Association members were granted patents in 1911 for the invention of the aileron and tricycle undercarriage — still major features on today's aircraft. Bell's reputation gave the bizarre field respectability, and his genius for publicity fueled interest in aeronautics throughout the country.

HYDROFOILS: In 1908, Bell turned to the problem of an airplane taking off from water and came across the hydrofoil

The tetrahedron shed.

The Cygnet. A powered kite, the *Cygnet* was towed by steamer into the wind on Baddeck Bay in 1907. U.S. Army Lt. Thomas E. Selfridge rode the kite (without the engine) as a volunteer passenger. It flew for seven minutes above the water.

idea, developed by an Italian, Forlanini. On their world tour in 1910, Bell and Mabel visited the inventor and rode in his boat on Lake Maggiore. Returning to Cape Breton, he built three hydrofoil boats which all crashed. However, one of them reached a speed of fifty miles an hour. After World War I, in 1919, he built the *HD-4*. Sixty feet long and heavily powered by aircraft engines, it reached 70.86 miles per hour, a world record which stood for ten years. The Naval Disarmament Conference caused development to be abandoned until our own times. Bell received patents for the hydrofoil a few months before his death in 1922.

EDUCATION OF THE DEAF AND GENETICS: When asked his profession, Bell always answered: "teacher of the deaf." He established a model school in Scotland in 1878 — which still exists — to apply his theories for bringing the deaf back *into* society. He passionately championed oral methods aided by lip reading, and opposed sign language. This caused a controversy which lasted for years. He wrote numerous articles and testified in America and Britain before many government bodies for his cause. The Volta Bureau collected and analyzed

Bell viewing the HD-4 in 1920.

An early effort to make the telephone more decorative as well as more compact can be seen in this souvenir of the Gay Nineties. The carbon transmitter is becoming less unwieldy, the receiver has been reduced in size so that it was called a "watch case" receiver and the ornate base reflects the taste of the era.

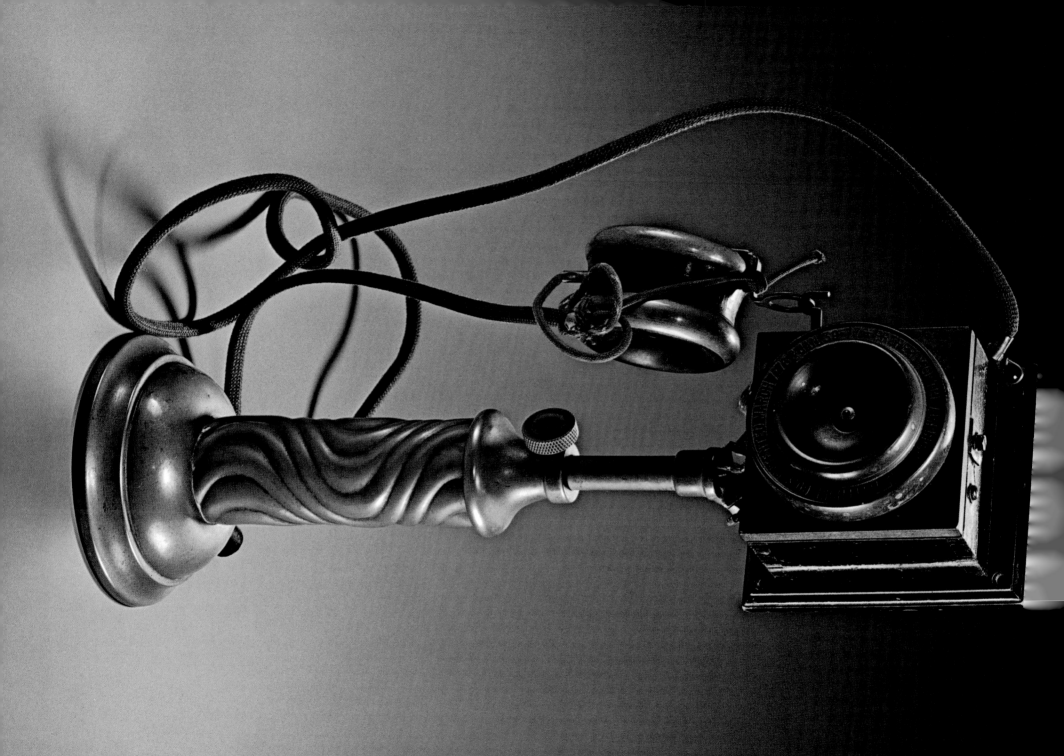

A rare photograph from the Horace Mann School for the Deaf in 1899. Notice Bell's picture and his biography on the board for study by the deaf children. Bell said of the school: "It is only right that it should be known that the telephone is one of the products of the work of the Horace Mann School for the Deaf in Boston and resulted from my attempts to benefit the children of this school."

Alexander Graham Bell with Helen Keller (seated) and her famous teacher, Anne Sullivan.

Bell studying sheep breeding.

"I believe in universal suffrage, without qualification of education, sex, color, or property." *Bell in 1901*

Fearful of the tendency for deaf persons to marry deaf partners when each knew only sign language, he wrote a controversial paper *On the Formation of a Deaf Variety of the Human Race*. Subject to great abuse at the time, his work was vindicated eventually and became a powerful force for efforts to integrate the deaf into normal society. He continually tried to expand their occupational opportunities and practiced what he preached. He established his old pupil, George Sanders, in the printing business and kept watch over his progress for many years. Bell's personal monetary contributions to deaf causes amounted to a half-million dollars.

His interest in heredity led him to selective breeding of sheep to improve wool and meat and to increase the probability of twin births. He produced some odd specimens, but the experiments proved commercially unsuccessful, though his flocks were remarkable enough to be taken over by the government researchers. His thorough records and methods of analysis, however, laid the basis for a great deal of later work in genetics. He was especially interested in longevity factors and was a power in the eugenics movement until it was captured by

enormous amounts of data on deafness through generations of families. Bell persuaded the U.S. Census to compile the data necessary to convince people of the problem's importance. He also invented the *audiometer* to test hearing in order to identify those people, especially children, suffering from early stages of the affliction. Helen Keller, deaf and blind, came to him at age seven, and Bell supervised her education under Annie Sullivan (the "Miracle Worker") until she graduated *cum laude* from Radcliffe. They remained lifelong friends.

155

fanatics and racists.

His abiding interest in educational methods led to his setting up the first Montessori classes in Canada at his summer residence in 1912. The first full-time Montessori School in America was established at his Washington home in the autumn of 1912, and Bell was elected first president of the Montessori Educational Association.

SUPPORT OF SCIENCE AS AN INSTITUTION OF SOCIETY: Bell gave financial support to A. A. Michelson, who precisely determined the velocity of light and performed the Michelson-Morley Experiment so important to Albert Einstein's relativity theory. A regent of the Smithsonian Institution, he took the job seriously, and early in his tenure saw the need for an authoritative journal of record and information. He organized, staffed and subsidized the publication *Science* in 1882, and it remains to this day the official organ of the American Association for the Advancement of Science.

Bell brought new life to the nearly defunct National Geo-

graphic Society on becoming its president in 1897. He infused his ideas and money and installed a future son-in-law as its first employee and editor. He started the *National Geographic Magazine* on its road to vast readership by insistence on pictures, crisp writing, reliable information and high-quality maps, all geared to topical events "occupying the public mind." This magazine has remained a prime source of scientific knowledge for the public since that time, and many brilliant children have been attracted to careers in science by exposure to its pages in early life.

SYMBOLS OF CONTRIBUTION: During his last forty years, Bell who had been so eager for recognition when a young, struggling inventor, was now inundated by honors of every conceivable kind. Twelve honorary doctorates (including Edinburgh and Oxford), scores of medals, and schools for the deaf named for him, all added a golden haze to the sunset of life. On his extensive travels to foreign countries — many times to Europe, but including trips to India, China, Australia, New

△ Bell in 1908 with a group of colleagues of the Aerial Experiment Association.

1913 Wall Set. The wall telephone becoming more compact. Instruments like these were in general service, forerunners of today's Home Interphone System. They provided intercommunication within the home and were advertised by Western Electric as the "greatest little step-savers that ever helped a housewife."

A Bell Family Album

Top row left to right: Alec and Mabel in December, 1885, with their two daughters, Elsie May (left), who later became Mrs. Gilbert H. Grosvenor, and Marian ("Daisy"), who later became Mrs. David Fairchild.

Alec and Mabel in the 1900's.

Four generations of Bells.

Bottom row left to right: Bell with his granddaughters.

Bell family gathering.

Bell in 1919 with his daughter, Elsie May.

Zealand, Mexico, Japan and South America — he was constantly astonished by the receptions his fame stimulated. In 1915, a movie producer included Bell in the list of the "ten most prominent men in America" and wished to film him for posterity. Bell declined. The yearning youth had finally achieved a surfeit of celebrity.

When he died of diabetes on August 2, 1922, it seemed more the end of an institution than the passing of a man. For the first — and last — time all telephone service in America was stopped for one minute as a tribute of respect for the visionary who had given it birth. His old rival, Edison, mellowed by the years, said, "My late friend, Alexander Graham Bell, whose world-famed invention annihilated time and space, brought the human family in closer touch." Mabel, comrade in life and death, joined her husband forever on that windswept Cape Breton peak five months later.

From Helen Keller's autobiography:

To

ALEXANDER GRAHAM BELL

Who has taught the deaf to speak
and enabled the listening ear to hear
speech from the Atlantic to the Rockies,
I Dedicate
this Story of My Life.

Burial scene August 4, 1922 on Beinn Bhreagh. Mabel insisted that the women wear white and the men their summer clothing as Alec hated mourning wear. Both the United States and British flags were raised on temporary poles. Today the grave site is marked with Bell's name, birth and death dates, notes that he was an "inventor" by vocation and includes the words he requested: "Died a Citizen of the United States".

Alexander Graham Bell's many-sided genius is commemorated in a remarkable and little-known museum in Baddeck, Cape Breton, Nova Scotia. The architectural theme of the tetrahedron, developed by Bell and applied in kite and airplane experiments, distinguishes the structure. Bell first visited Baddeck in 1885. Enthralled by the area's scenic resemblance to his native Scotland, he built a summer "second" home there in 1892 calling it "Beinn Bhreagh" or "Beautiful Mountain". There he built laboratories and workshops, assembling a mixed group of young, brilliant Canadian and American researchers. Inspired and mostly financed by Bell himself, the group worked on experiments in powered flight, ailerons, propellers, and landing carriages. Bell continued to develop new methods for teaching the deaf, began research in eugenics, ocean sounding devices, air-conditioning and hydrofoil boat construction. "The inventor," Bell once remarked, "is a man who looks around the world and is not contented with things as they are. He wants to improve whatever he sees, he wants to benefit the world; he is haunted by an idea, the spirit of invention possesses him, seeking materialization."

Bell Museum interior. Constructed in 1954-55 on a site donated by the Government of Nova Scotia and maintained by the Canadian National and Historic Parks Branch of the Department of Indian affairs and Northern Development.

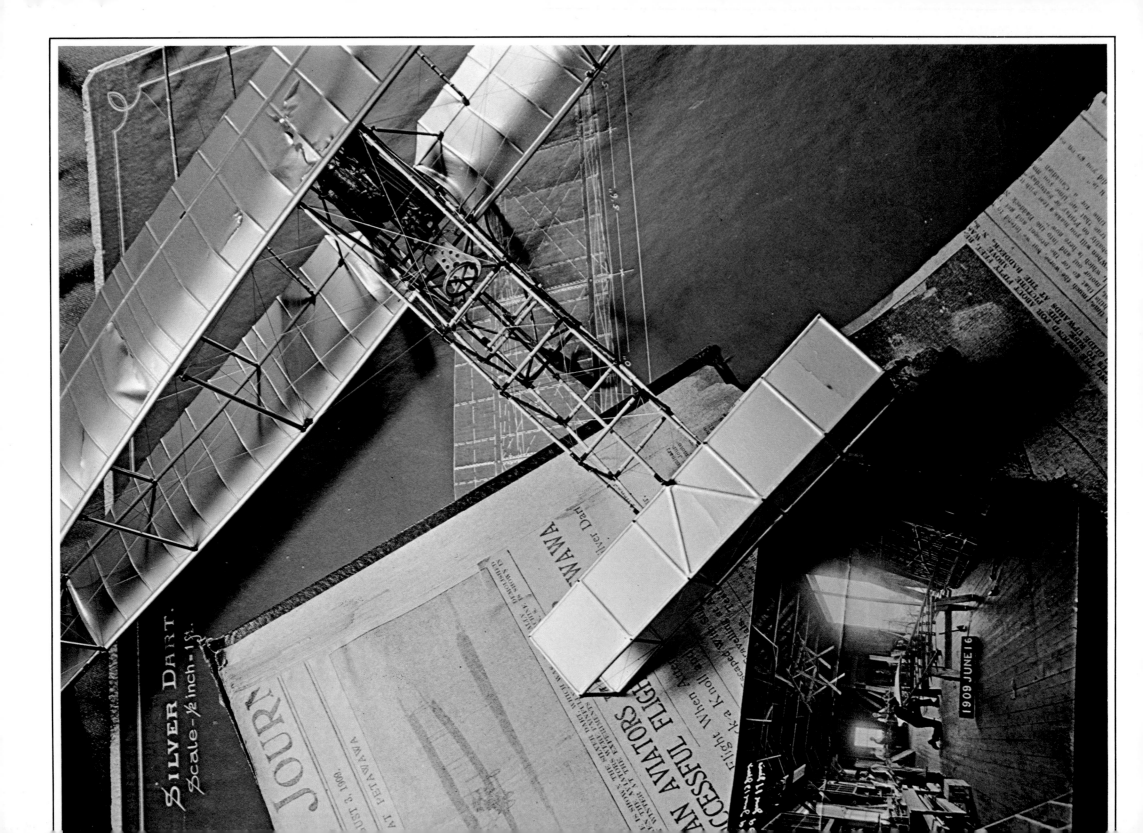

Flight

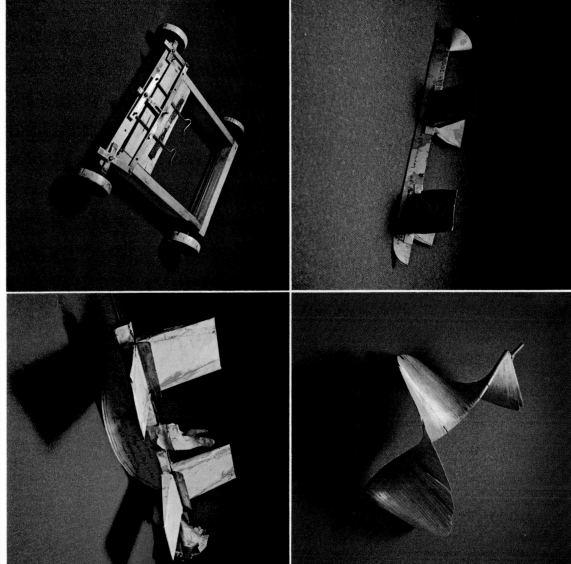

Model and blueprints of the "Silver Dart" first flown for a half mile, 30 feet over Baddeck Bay, by J. A. D. McCurdy, on February 23, 1909. The plane used Bell's aileron and undercarriage ideas and was powered by a water-cooled V-8 engine designed by Glenn Curtiss. Later that year, McCurdy flew a variation of the Silver Dart, the "Baddeck", it crashed on landing. McCurdy suffered a broken nose and the Canadian Army decided that the airplane was not practical for military purposes.

Bell's flight experiments were conducted by the Aerial Experiment Association financed by Mabel. Members of the group included F. W. ("Casey") Baldwin, J. A. D. McCurdy, Glenn H. Curtiss and Thomas Selfridge. (clockwise) Paper model plane for children; model of wooden propeller; "push-principle" model plane; landing carriage.

The Sanders Reader

Example of a "reader" Bell prepared in the early 1870's for his young deaf pupil, Georgie Sanders. Bell pasted color prints into a blank book and wrote out a children's story.

Visible Speech

Melville Bell's "Visible Speech" printed in a children's book. The notebooks were used by Alexander Graham Bell to work out ideas. Often he wrote messages and comments to Mabel on their walks. (r.) A typewriter adapted for printing "Visible Speech" characters.

The Sanders Reader

Example of a "reader" Bell prepared in the early 1870's for his young deaf pupil, Georgie Sanders. Bell pasted color prints into a blank book and wrote out a children's story.

Visible Speech

Melville Bell's "Visible Speech" printed in a children's book. The notebooks were used by Alexander Graham Bell to work out ideas. Often he wrote messages and comments to Mabel on their walks. (r.) A typewriter adapted for printing "Visible Speech" characters.

Flight

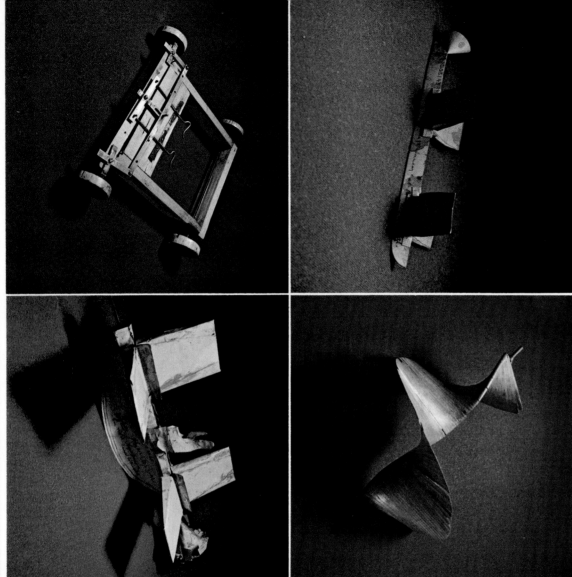

Model and blueprints of the "Silver Dart" first flown for a half mile, 30 feet over Baddeck Bay, by J. A. D. McCurdy, on February 23, 1909. The plane used Bell's aileron and undercarriage ideas and was powered by a water-cooled V-8 engine designed by a Curtiss. Later that year, McCurdy flew a variation of the Silver Dart, the "Baddeck", it crashed on landing. McCurdy suffered a broken nose and the Canadian Army decided that the airplane was not practical for military purposes.

Bell's flight experiments were conducted by the Aerial Experiment Association financed by Mabel. Members of the group included F. W. ("Casey") Baldwin, J. A. D. McCurdy, Glenn H. Curtiss and Thomas Selfridge. (clockwise) Paper model plane for children; model of wooden propeller; "push-principle" model plane; landing carriage.

BEINN BHREACH
RECORDER
VOL. 7

Beinn Bhreach Recorder

Admiral Amara and the four five-nippled Native
taken by John McNeil.

McNeil.

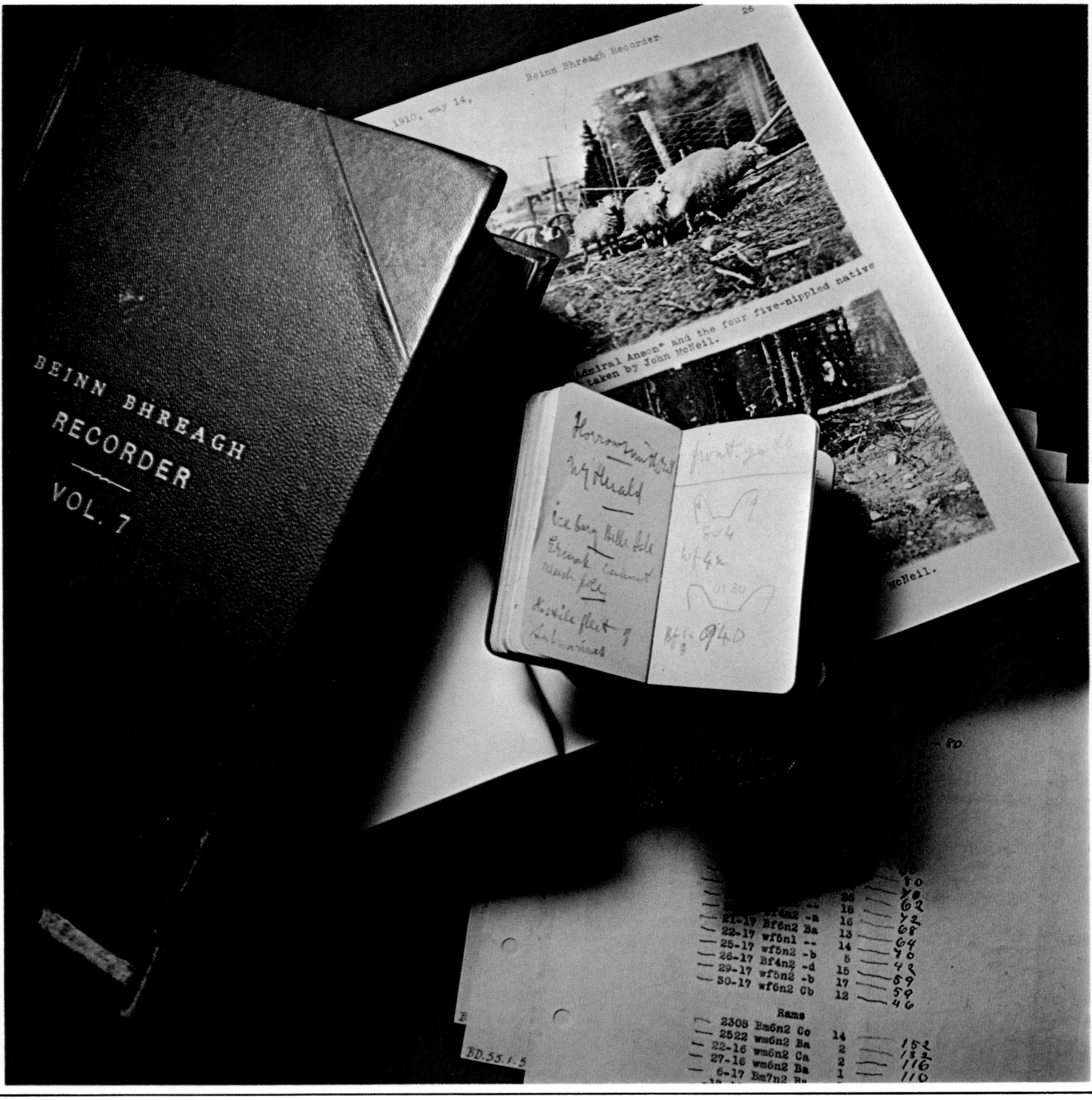

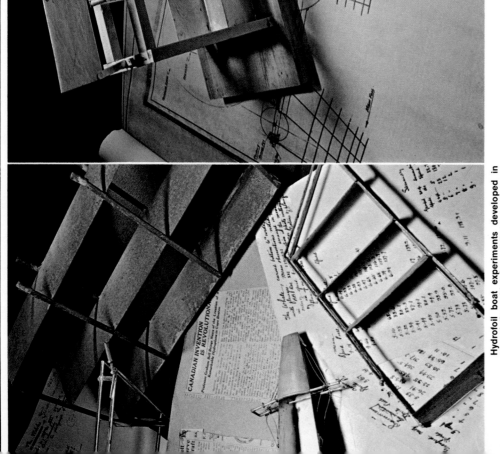

Hydrofoil boat experiments developed in association with "Casey" Baldwin. Bell applied his aileron and propeller experiments to create the fastest boat in the world, the "HD-4" which achieved a speed of 70.86 miles per hour in 1919 on Baddeck Bay. Their research began in 1906 when Bell said: "Why should we not have heavier than water machines as well as lighter than water?"

A "bug" constructed by Bell to discover how an insect skitters over water at high speeds without sinking.

Model of air-conditioner built for his Washington, D.C. home in the 1900's using the principle of ducts and compressed air. An early advocate of artificial home cooling, Bell suffered from heat rashes and headaches. "I fear the [United] States in the hot weather," he once remarked.

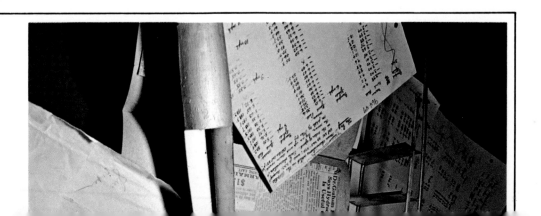

Tetrahedron

The tetrahedron design came to him as he attempted to overcome wind resistance in kite flying. Manned and powered flight needed a stronger internal structure than box or flat construction. "Avoid rectangular elements," he noted in 1902, "let everything be built up of equilateral triangles." (top right) A tetrahedron made of skin with his jottings; (bottom left) Aluminum "joints" to hinge together "cells" of triangles; (bottom right) Paper tetrahedron cells Bell made to see what variation in form he could achieve. He hoped that the tetrahedron would be used in bridge and building construction using standardized joints.

CHAPTER ⊕ 10

10

A TRANSCENDENT LEGACY OF PASSION AND PURPOSE

While Bell had explored the possibilities of his creative genius, the telephone lived a life of its own.

The Portuguese proverb, "God writes straight with crooked lines," defines the pattern of events in Theodore Vail's apparently random activities between his retirement from the telephone business at 42 and his return in 1907, at 62. Everything he did and learned in those years tempered and prepared him for the heroic tasks awaiting his talents. Vail mastered the *craft* of management and now used it to realize a *personal* vision. In this realm, he is more akin to a great artist than to our stereotype of a cold, professional bureaucrat. The intellectual and human aspects of his grand design remain the foundation structure of telecommunications in our day.

Following his resignation, he embarked on a two-and-a-half year journey all over Europe to restore his health. He organized several ventures — mining and municipal heating — none of which was really successful. He poured money and energy into his Vermont farm, the emotional base to which he constantly returned for physical and spiritual renewal. One of his lifelong passionate delights was to drive a carriage, pulled by spirited Kentucky horses, "four-in-hand." This is a skill which demands stamina, courage, will and acute sensitivity, both to innate capacities of the team and the changing conditions they encounter. The analogy to management — a word first used in horsemanship — is extremely close. Toward the end of his life, he told his biographer, "When I take hold of a thing I want the men under me to realize that they are doing the work and I am taking the responsibility." He never wavered from that view. His reputation as a host was legendary, and he enjoyed the

company of all sorts and conditions of people. Typical weekend guests at the farm would include businessmen, painters, musicians, writers, educators — together with neighbors and close friends — all participating in picnics, concerts, drives and dinners. He often played the large pipe organ for their entertainment. Vail handled correspondence and conversation simultaneously and never appeared worried, pressed for time or uninterested in people with problems. He collected paintings and books, read classics and current works, was fluent in French, and seemed to know everyone from village schoolchildren to heads of state.

In 1894, one of his guests asked his advice about the South American electricity business. Vail went to Argentina, "stopping off" in London to arrange financing. Commuting between America, Argentina and Europe, he rescued the properties and built several successful power systems and street railways. By the time he returned in 1907, he had accumulated about three million dollars. Throughout the period, he transformed his farm into a model establishment and made a gift of it to the state of Vermont as an agricultural training school. Romantic and practical, gregarious and purposeful, the two driving forces of his character were a belief in the necessity of organization for real progress and a passionate concern for the human effects and conditions attendant to any organized effort. *VAIL TAKES COMMAND*: After absorbing all the facts available, Vail worked out complex problems of combining men, money, machines and methods for himself. His favorite card game was a complicated form of solitaire using two decks of cards he always carried with him. Characteristically, he never

Vail in the 1910's.

minded an audience while he played out the game. Once he decided on a course, he applied two abilities to an almost uncanny degree: his sense of timing and his selection of specific acts which symbolized to individuals sincere concern for their welfare and need of their help.

1907: Over 1,300,000 immigrants arrived in America in that year. President Theodore Roosevelt claims Philippine Islands may lead to war with Japan.

Soon after arriving on May 1, 1907, he was told by Baring Brothers, bankers of London, that they had too many unsold telephone bonds on hand and wanted no more. Vail replied, "Don't worry, you will get rid of *those* and want more of our bonds before the year is out." The sophisticated financier remarked later to one of his colleagues that he felt sorry for Vail, who did not realize the impossible situation he was in. Foreseeing, as few did, the nation's coming economic storms and ignoring all "expert advice," Vail announced an immense

Vail and Bell meet for the first time on the steps of the National Geographic Society's Washington, D.C. building.

offer of stock to existing stockholders. To the amazement of his people, it was an astonishing success. When financial panic gripped the entire country four months later, Vail had in hand the resources for reconstruction. In December, he was met before breakfast in London by the same Baring Brothers' man who now wanted all the telephone bonds he could get.

Knowing that the restoration of confidence was crucial, he set up an accounting and reporting system which would tell accurate conditions quickly and in time for action. He cut back on nonessentials but put the savings immediately to work on long-range programs. He organized the scattered engineering forces into a central research and development group to lead the technological assault on the problems of growth and service quality. He made the acquaintance of all senior management personnel throughout the country, often taking them on his yacht for meetings and *sometimes not letting them off until a policy had been hammered out and agreed to.* They became his

10

Vail sailing in the 1910's.

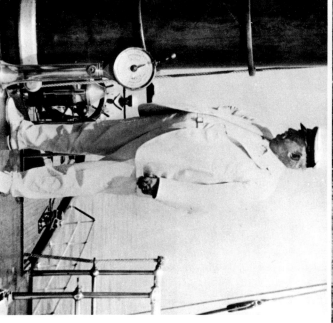

Vail photographing a picnic group at the Vermont farm.

Vail with favorite dogs.

Twenty Million Voices

A PERFECT understanding by the public of the management and full scope of the Bell Telephone System can have but one effect, and that a most desirable one —a marked betterment of the service.

American Telephone & Telegraph Company

And Its Associated Bell Companies

One Policy—One System
Universal Service

UNITING OVER 3,000,000 TELEPHONES

friends as well as colleagues, infused with his principles and vision. His first annual report, issued seven months after arrival, was too frank for his associates. He refused to moderate his words and said, "No, we will lay our cards on the table; there is never anything to be gained by concealment." To investigating bodies, state and federal, he responded in person, saying, "What is it you would like to know? We will show you anything you want to see, and do anything you ask. Just tell us what you want."

In 1908, his vision was expressed in widespread advertising for public consideration: ONE POLICY, ONE SYSTEM, UNIVERSAL SERVICE was the headline slogan in large type.

Child labor in mills in the early 1900's. The new role of women in offices and factories stirred public awareness of the need for improved working conditions. The Bell System was one of the first mass employers to pioneer in vocational training and employee welfare programs. Photograph by Lewis Hine.

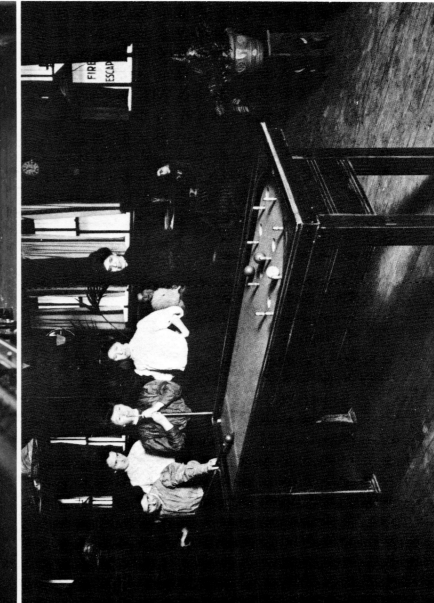

Illinois Bell Telephone operators' recreation room in 1907.

Women's Suffrage Parade, 1910's. △

His idea was that every person should have access to a telephone, and all telephones should have quick access to each other. He discontinued the policy of battling independent companies and worked for cooperation and consolidation of *service* to the public. To timid colleagues, fearing government attack, he replied, "Take the public into confidence and you win the confidence of the public."

1909: National Association for the Advancement of Colored People (NAACP) founded.

He insisted that employees be courteous to customers and provided rest lounges and restaurants for women operators. In 1913, he established a pension and benefit plan for all em-

ployees and built convalescent homes for their recovery from illness. Employees were enabled to buy company stock on the installment plan. A veteran worker in Chicago, remembering those years, said, "Mr. Vail not only knew the telephone business, he knew the *world's* business, and that restored confidence."

One part of the vision failed. For many years Vail had seen the public advantages in combining telegraph and telephone service. In 1909, Western Union was in disastrous condition from years of neglect. Vail acquired the company, became its president, and proceeded to resuscitate its 25,000 locations, raising its public image. He ordered all the offices cleaned and

painted, made service innovations such as reduced-rate night and weekend letters, encouraged customers to send telegrams conveniently by telephone, combined billing, visited employees of all ranks to discern their problems, increased wages by 50 percent, made loans available to those in need, and instituted a pension and benefit plan. Before the days of radio, ocean telephone cables and satellites, his advertisements could truthfully say:

When you lift the receiver of a Bell Telephone and call "Western Union" you are in communication with all the world.

Morale and business soared. But in 1913, the Federal government believed that the consolidation violated antitrust laws. Vail forthwith divested Western Union, by then made

The first transcontinental telephone call, New York to San Francisco January 25, 1915. Bell is surrounded by Bell System officials and Mayor John Purroy Mitchell of New York. Above Bell is a portrait of Vail, who participated in the ceremonies from Jekyll Island, Georgia, where he was recuperating from a fall.

The San Francisco connection of the first transcontinental call. Thomas A. Watson is seen with a group of Pacific Telephone and Telegraph officers. Seated third from left is Thomas B. Doolittle who perfected a process for making a type of copper wire which speeded early long distance development.

vigorous after four years of his attention, from the Bell System. Personal letters from telegraph employees, thanking him for what he had done for their lives and company, cushioned the old dream's disappointment.

MILESTONES: Vail lost no time in driving his technologists to their limits and beyond. After Denver had been linked to New York, in 1911, Vail demanded a grand push to the Pacific. During a discussion of efforts and resources needed, some of the board members were afraid the venture would be unprofitable. Vail ended the meeting with: "Oh, well, if it is a good thing, let's do it, anyhow." They did, in 1915. Always interested in frontiers, Vail in 1915 staggered his exhausted engineers with a new problem: use wireless (radio) to connect European telephones to the telephones of America. J. J. Carty,

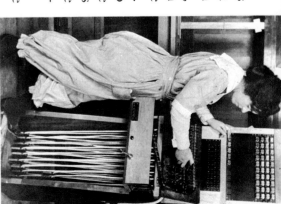

Pacific Telephone Company motor vehicle, San José, 1912. The Company's total investment in automotive equipment at this time was only about $20,000.

Restoring communications after the San Francisco Earthquake.

First unit of Telephone Operators sent to France during World War I. June, 1918.

△ The final pole needed to connect the transcontinental line is mounted on June 17, 1914 at Wendover, Utah on the Nevada-Utah border. The job required extraordinary efforts and was acclaimed as one of the great technical achievements of the day.

the chief engineer who had begun as a boy mechanic in Bell's early days, asked for $125,000 to attempt the job. Vail gave him double that! With World War I on, the work had to be done in secret — and was. After frantic days and nights of work, wireless telephone calls were effected from New York to San Diego and Honolulu. The French government "loaned" the Eiffel Tower, and the U.S. Navy their Virginia installations. On October 21, 1915, communication took place from Paris to Honolulu. At a dinner on March 7, 1916, celebrating the fortieth anniversary of Bell's patent, there were demonstrations of the frontier achievement. Vail and Bell sat next to one another at the head table. It was their first meeting in thirty-five years.

Foreseeing America's entry into the World War long before

A Frame Switchboard and installer, Emeryville, California, 1918.

others who believed campaign promises, he raised $130 million of new bonds and stock soon after President Wilson's reelection, again ignoring "expert" financial advice. When in 1917 war did come, the company was ready to make a major contribution. He also completed construction of the New York building which still houses the headquarters of the Bell System, and whose architecture and decoration bear the unmistakable stamp of his taste in every detail. A three-day test of wartime readiness in 1916 demonstrated that the telephone and telegraph system already in existence could handle alone all communications required to run the defense establishment throughout the entire nation. As soon as war was declared by the United States, volunteer telephone battalions from Bell personnel were formed for the Army Signal Corps. Many sailed

World War I Western Electric "Camp Switchboard".

immediately with General Pershing to France. Twenty-five thousand employees, in fourteen battalions, entered the ranks, and more than half served overseas. Women operators staffed the 273 exchanges built by these forces in France. This example of speed and organization heavily influenced the French postwar reconstruction of their communications system. Vail saw all his people off to war and sent along hampers of delicacies from his farm.

1917: Bolsheviks seize power in Russia. Lenin proclaims: "Soviets plus electricity equals socialism."

On July 24, 1918, President Wilson proclaimed that all telephone and telegraph operations would be under possession and control of the Post Office Department supervised by the Postmaster General, Albert S. Burleson, an outspoken, ardent champion of government ownership. Vail went to Washington, confessing feelings of total helplessness to his colleagues. To everyone's surprise, Burleson and Vail quickly saw that they respected one another's views and agreed on full cooperation. On July 30, 1919, the government returned the company to its

Mobile radio telephone, 1924.

△ Black Protest March, Fifth Avenue, New York City, ca. 1912. Industrialization was the chief factor in moving large numbers of blacks away from rural areas to large cities.

Western Electric's winning girls' relay team, △ Chicago, 1924.

Vail's successor, H.B. Thayer, talking from △ △ his New York office to England by radio telephone on January 14, 1923. The research involved was done jointly by AT&T's research department — later Bell Telephone Laboratories — and RCA.

Vail and "Four-in-Hand", Boston, 1910's.

owners, and Burleson considered Vail's performance worthy of a medal. In regard to compensation for use, he recalled Vail's offer as in total contrast to that of railroad presidents. Vail said, "You fix it, and I'll be satisfied."

He became chairman of the board of A.T. & T. in June 1919; and Harry Thayer, his longtime friend and the head of Western Electric, became president. Just before his death, he said, "I have been worried for three years over what would happen if I suddenly went out and the wrong man was put in my place. Thayer is a great comfort to me." Thus, he achieved the final task of a corporate leader, ensuring a sound succession. Early in April, 1920, Vail fell seriously ill at his summer home on Jekyl Island, Georgia, and was taken to Johns Hopkins Hospital in Baltimore for treatment. After five days he died, on April 16.

In his last hours, he gave brisk orders, not to subordinates, but to remembered horses driven four-in-hand. Even in death, life remained an adventure calling for action and nerve.

Vail's accomplishment was immense, but his enduring legacy was a philosophy. He believed that a large business must

find its legitimacy in service to the public. He saw that regulation of prices by public bodies was essential to protect the public interest, and that standards of fairness must seek a balance between those who used the service and those who provided the resources necessary for its existence, growth and improvement. He saw that only by public consent could such a complex and pervasive entity exist at all, and that information about the conduct of its affairs must be freely given and criticism studied. And with it all, continual improvement in speed, access, quality and efficiency must be embraced almost as a faith.

These beliefs are still held by his legatees.

THE BREAKOUT: Vail's organizing genius positioned all the forces needed for strategic advance toward his dream of what should be a *communications* system worthy of the nation.

Thayer was the first of "up-from-the-ranks" chief executives (he began as a shipping clerk) and that tradition has remained unbroken since his time. He carried out the consolidation of disparate local operating companies into larger state and re-gional entities. The backlog of unfilled orders — caused by the war — was eliminated. The annual "nine-dollar dividend," bedrock of financial reputation through depression and war, was established in 1921. In 1925, after several regroupings, research and development forces were combined to form Bell Telephone Laboratories. Application of technical advance, like many tributaries feeding a great river, were channeled to the public's service. Exotic things, like air-to-ground and ship-to-shore telephones, and radio broadcasting, as well as improved amplifiers for telephone calls, grew from intensive research on vacuum tubes. Newspapers were linked by press associations using Bell wires to send news and pictures; the massive conversions to dial phones began; radio stations across the country were linked into networks; and WEAF, a powerful broadcasting station built by Bell engineers, began operating in the telephone headquarters building. This station pioneered the first "commercials," sports programs and national election returns. By the end of Thayer's term, innovations in transmission and switching methods allowed a long distance call to be

set up in about two minutes.

In 1925, Walter Gifford, age 40, Harvard graduate and former payroll clerk, became president. He led the company for the next 23 years. Like Watson, he was born in Salem, Massachusetts, but he represented a new era in the nation and the company, when managers would increasingly come to business after university schooling. Gifford presided over and initiated policy changes which, though lacking in glamour, profoundly affected the future course of the enterprise. He focused energies and attention on providing basic telephone service, and abandoned some ventures that the outpouring of inventions had established through pioneering communications achievements. These had become so diverse, that they would have astonished even Vail's imagination.

1920: Over 8,000,000 automobiles in America.

The Bell System left the radio business, selling its properties and patents to the National Broadcasting Company. The first sound motion pictures and high fidelity phonographs were developed by Bell engineers. After a heady period of Hollywood ventures, this activity was divested, as well as the more mundane electrical supplies business, which was sold to its

The Perils of Prosperity. Agents destroying illicit beer during Prohibition, 1920's.

employees. The first public demonstration of long-distance television took place in 1927, a conversation between Herbert Hoover in Washington and Gifford in New York. (Color TV was transmitted a few years later.) Transatlantic telephone service was inaugurated, using short-wave radio, and Mexico was added to the international network in 1927. At Dallas, on October 20, 1927, Gifford addressed a meeting of the government commissioners who regulated telephone rates, investment and profits. There he stated a fundamental Bell System policy: "The most telephone service and the best, at the least cost consistent with financial safety."

In 1929, a symbol of the telephone's pervasiveness occurred when Herbert Hoover became the first president of the United States to have a phone installed on his desk. (His predecessors had used an enclosed booth outside the executive office.) A few months later, the coaxial cable was patented. It made network television possible and also furnished a medium for carrying large numbers of long distance calls in a small space. The negative-feedback amplifier, an invention essential to every area of electronics where distortion must be minimized, was patented in 1930. Bell scientists also brought something to sports

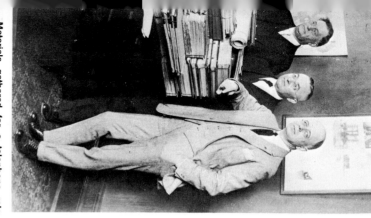

Materials gathered for a telephone rate hearing case in Atlanta, Georgia, 1920's.

△ W.S. Gifford, seated before original instruments through which Bell transmitted speech in 1876, opens transatlantic telephone service to Paris, March 28, 1928.

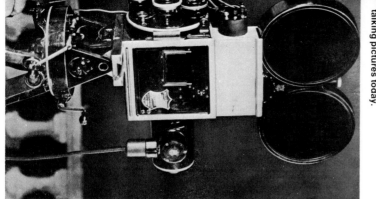

Lee De Forest developed Audion amplifier into a "glow tube" (1920-21) making possible sound-recording on film. The basic amplifier tube remains an essential part of talking pictures today.

The Dance, a period piece of the Age. ▽

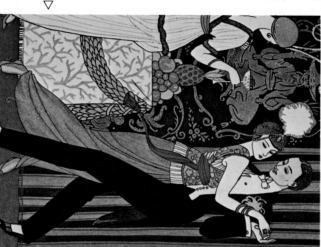

Charles A. Lindbergh and the "Spirit of St. Louis" after his historic New York to Paris non-stop solo flight. Photograph taken May 31, 1927.

with their "photo-finish" timing apparatus, first used in 1932. Teletypewriter Exchange Service was introduced in 1931; the first round-the-world telephone call was made in 1935; and a Nobel Prize in 1937 was won by Bell Laboratories' Davisson, for experimental discovery of the wave nature of electrons. Countries in every part of the world were added monthly to the overseas telephone network in rapid succession after 1928. Rates were progressively reduced as volume grew. A radio altimeter — which tells the height above ground — was developed for use by aircraft in 1938 and was the first public application of radar principles. Throughout the two decades before World War II, constant improvements and new designs in switching machines were rapidly placed in service.

1928: Herbert Hoover, Republican Presidential Candidate: "We in America today are nearer the final triumph over poverty than ever before in the history of any land."

DEPRESSION: Gifford steadily guided the business through the economic slump caused by the Great Depression of the 1930s. While other companies drastically cut back throughout the nation's trauma, he maintained payment of the nine-dollar

dividend to the stockholders, furnishing a stabilizing economic force, retaining the reputation of the "widows and orphans" stock, and laying the foundation for confidence when recovery came later. To a business accustomed only to constant growth, he brought humane retrenchment measures, keeping as many employed as possible, some of whom even sold telephones by canvassing door-to-door to help keep their fellow workers on the job.

Besides coping with a period of unprecedented hardship and daily economic disaster, Gifford was confronted by an attack aimed at the heart of his company. One of the New Deal federal agencies set up by President Franklin D. Roosevelt in hopes of bringing vigorous response to the national crisis was the Federal Communications Commission, established in 1934. It was charged by Congress with regulating and supervising the conduct of all broadcasting, telephone and telegraph operations. One of its first acts was to initiate a comprehensive, public investigation of the Bell System. The commissioner responsible for carrying it out stated that for ten years there had been many demands on Congress for government ownership or a full-scale investigation of the industry to satisfy the public interest. The work of the investigators consumed four years, and their findings fill a densely-packed 800-page book. There was no corner of history, no complaint, no suggestion of misjudgment, nor alleged abuse which was not followed up with diligence and zeal. Admittedly, a "natural monopoly" which sprang from the nature of a unified system of inter-communication, the company suffered a grave disadvantage in a culture where competition and rivalry are held to be the mainspring of economic progress. Gifford and his people had to prove that telephone service was an exception to conventional economic doctrines and justified an exceptional philosophy to carry out its commitments and responsibilities to the nation.

1938: Stalin terms Russian Communist Party "purge" and farm collectivization drives "very successful." An estimated 30 million Soviet people killed between 1929-1938. Hitler and British Prime Minister proclaim "Peace in our time" at Munich.

They succeeded for the most part in meeting the awesome burden of proof, and the 1938 government report was not as antagonistic as critics desired. The general public maintained throughout a favorable attitude to the service. When the imminence of World War II came to preoccupy attention of

the nation's leadership, a strong communications system was deemed so vital for the effort ahead that the Justice Department postponed its proposed antitrust suit against the Bell System. The suit had its origins in certain allegations of the Commission's investigation and was reactivated only at war's end, when the safety of the nation was once more assured.

WORLD WAR II: With doctrinal controversy suspended "for the duration," the Bell System was now charged to make maximum contributions to the country's defense capability. Three major types of tasks were involved: meet the greatly increased demands for regular telephone service to support the unprecedented mobilization of the economy and its people; deploy scientists and engineers to development of communications and weapons systems required in modern land, sea and air warfare; and manufacture both the new military apparatus in enormous quantities, together with all the transmission and switching facilities needed to handle the explosion of usage and establishment of new communities. All this had to be done under conditions of material shortages, financial stringency and loss of 70,000 skilled personnel to the combat forces.

It was done.

As training camps mushroomed across the nation, communications facilities appeared on the scene with the first

New York Governor Franklin D. Roosevelt campaigning for President in 1932. FDR's New Deal greatly changed the role of government in the economy, began Social Security, encouraged labor union organization but never ended the Depression's massive unemployment until the start of World War II.

Dustbowl farmers on the move during the Great Depression years.

The Crash as seen through the press.

△ Great New England Storm. On September 21, 1938 a vicious hurricane struck the eastern seaboard, from the New Jersey shores to Boston and Cape Cod. Winds were recorded at 130 miles per hour. Tidal waves, exceeding 25 feet in height, were driven ashore at over 50 miles per hour. Thousands of homes, ships and bridges were completely destroyed. In what is now considered the greatest natural disaster in American history, the storm killed more people (680) than the Great Chicago Fire and San Francisco Earthquake combined. Over 20,000 miles of telephone and electric wires were damaged. Communications stopped in greater New England. Bell System workers, using standardized equipment from most operating companies all over the country, raced to the disaster scene. More than 3,000 men and women using over 600 vehicles, 400 miles of cable, 31,000 poles, 72 million feet of wire and 50 carloads of Western Electric equipment established normal service in record time. After the storm, a contemporary said: "The face of New England had been changed... But one had seen, had listened in darkness, had realized the community rallying."

bulldozer. Scientists used knowledge and methods laboriously acquired over many years in improving civil communications, to design entire systems of equipment for combat conditions. They trained thousands of people from the armed forces in their use. Western Electric worked round the clock, turning out a river of hardware that went to every area of the great conflict. They produced half of all radar sets made during the war. Radios of every size for tanks, planes and artillery; radar systems; ultrahigh frequency and microwave techniques; flight trainers; submarine detection; artillery and mine fuses; military and naval fire-control systems; metallurgy for improved gun barrels; telephone and teletypewriter apparatus suitable for desert, jungle and Arctic; and a host of devices and components for other industries called forth theoretical, inventive and constructive skills working together to the harshest deadlines of survival. In 1945, when the war ended, over 1,200 major defense projects had been completed.

1945: Over 70,000 Bell System people served in the armed forces.

One innovation, based on Bell System laboratory work begun in the 1920s, proved to have profound effects on all future manufacturing in the world. Statistical theories and methods for controlling and assuring *quality* were widely applied to war production and are now standard equipment for managing any process, human or technical. (Following the war, Japan made it the cornerstone of an economic policy designed to secure a worldwide reputation for excellence, precision and reliability of their products.)

POSTWAR CHALLENGES: The war had done what political measures had not: fueled the economic recovery from the Depression. Widespread fears of peacetime collapse proved unfounded. Wartime shortages of everything formerly unemployed people (now defense workers) wanted to spend their money on — like cars, homes, food, clothing, schooling and residential telephones — forced them to postpone demand and accumulate funds which flooded on to the economic scene. Price control and rationing ended quickly, and as uniforms were laid aside, families formed, schools burst with veterans, civilian employment increased, and postponed desires were

1937 "300" Type Desk Set. An innovation in desk set design was the placing of the bell in the base of this model. Earlier versions were made of metal but plastic was substituted in the early 1940's. This set was manufactured in vast quantities to supply the unprecedented demand for telephone service which followed World War II.

1956 Wall Telephone, a return to the traditional placement. The same year the first transatlantic undersea telephone cable was laid for the Long Lines Department. Overseas calling increased dramatically. △

M-9 Gun Director (in trailer mount at right) being demonstrated in Murray Hill, New Jersey during World War II. The gun director was the first application of the electronic analogue computer. It played an important role in shooting down most of the German Buzz Bombs aimed at London and Antwerp. The technology, which saved countless lives, was conceived by Bell Laboratories.

10

gradually realized. The exposure to telephone use of millions on the move during the war years, the boom in housing, and the low, pre-war prices of telephone service, which would take years to increase through the difficult processes of public commission hearings, all combined to bring millions of new orders for service. A decade of backbreaking effort occurred before instant service installation and high quality were achieved. The gruelling process of obtaining price relief, when the cost of wages and materials rose competitively, kept the investor at a disadvantage. Yet confidence in the business was so high and technology so fruitful that necessary funds for immense construction flowed in constantly, year after year.

The antitrust case, postponed by Pearl Harbor, was resumed in 1949 and settled in 1956 by a "consent decree" when a federal court approved terms and conditions agreed upon by both government and business. Instead of severing the Western Electric manufacturing capability from the integrated Bell System — a primary demand of antitrust lawyers — the company agreed to confine itself to common carrier communications, to manufacture only products needed by Bell companies and the government, to make all patents held up to 1956 available to anyone without charge, and to promise that all future patents would be freely available at reasonable royalties.

In 1947, the first *nationwide* telephone strike occurred lasting 44 days and involving nearly 400,000 employees. Soon after, the National Federation of Telephone Workers, organized in

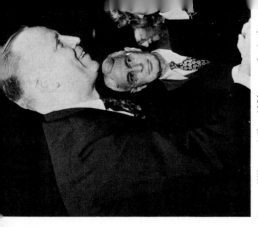

Leroy Wilson at the 1950 annual stockholder meeting.

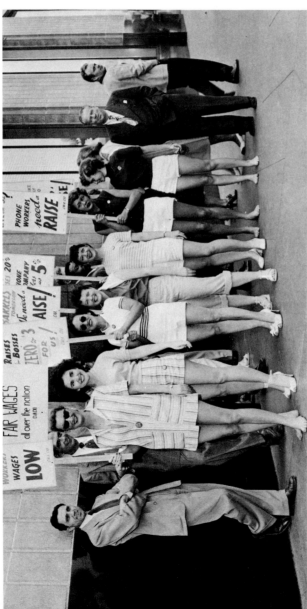

Communications Workers of America (AFL-CIO) during a 1951 Hollywood, California strike. The CWA represents the majority of unionized telephone workers in the Bell system and Independent telephone companies. Its motto is: "A National Union in the National Interest."

A CWA convention, 1971.

1959 Princess® Telephone, a compact "new look" with an illuminated dial. It lights up when the receiver is lifted.
®Registered Trademark of AT&T Co.

Cleo F. Craig (third from left, foreground) presenting 50-millionth telephone to President Dwight D. Eisenhower, the White House, November 18, 1953.

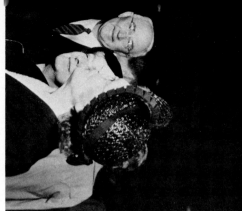

1937, was transformed into the dominant telephone union, Communications Workers of America. The second major union is the International Brotherhood of Electrical Workers which, at the turn of the century, began to organize various telephone crafts. There is also an alliance of several independent unions.

1951: The Brady Dentons of Saginaw, Michigan became AT&T's one millionth share holders.

In 1948, three Bell Laboratories men invented the transistor, which unlocked the gates to our modern electronic era, and for which they received the Nobel Prize. That same year Gifford's tenure ended, and Leroy Wilson, age 47 and up-from-the-ranks from Indiana, assumed command until his death three years later. Network television began in 1948, using coaxial cable, and rapidly reached across the country, stimulating the production of mass audience programs for nationwide viewing, thus setting off the media revolution of our time.

Direct distance dialing by customers — eliminating the need for operator intervention — required massive construction and grew rapidly as entire cities and states were converted to its use at one stroke in the small hours of a Sunday morning. Microwave radio methods, diverted to war use, were refocussed on telephone service, and beginning in 1948, their line-of-sight relay towers began to be seen on local promontories. The first of several transcontinental microwave systems was completed by 1951. Cleo Craig, an electrical engineer and

179

personnel expert born in Missouri, assumed the presidency on Wilson's death in 1951. New models of switching apparatus were installed and work was started to use electronic computer technology — begun in Bell Labs — for the service of the future. In 1956, the first transatlantic cable for telephone service to Great Britain was completed. Its improved quality and reliability triggered rapid growth in overseas calling. An undersea cable to Alaska was finished a few months later, a second Atlantic cable to France and Germany was under way, and Hawaii was joined by ocean cable to the mainland.

Frederick Kappel, 54, of Minnesota, succeeded Craig as president in 1956, and vigorously led the System for the next eleven years. When he assumed office, there were 50 million U.S. telephones, and 49 million in the rest of the world. He supervised 638,000 employees and was responsible to a million-and-a-half stockholders. In 1959, Kappel raised the $9 dividend, paid without interruption for 37 years, to $9.90, laying the financial groundwork for the advances required in the next decade.

MARKETING: With basic service caught up, Kappel expanded Vail's idea of Universal Service to include an array of services and instruments aimed at satisfying customers' individual preferences and needs. Color and button telephones, as well as systems designed for specific business and government operations, were designed and made commercially available. The first electronic exchange was installed in Illinois in 1960 and was capable of a wide range of customer-oriented automatic features, such as transferring a call to another number, repertory dialing, "call waiting" signals and so on.

In 1960, Bell engineers bounced telephone signals off a large metallic balloon set in space by a rocket and talked from New Jersey to California. Work on communications satellites followed rapidly, and a specially designed ship was built for laying ocean cables. In 1962, Bellcomm, Inc. was organized at the request of the government to perform the systems engineering function for Project Apollo moon landings. The same year, Bell's Telstar, the world's first communications satellite, rocketed into orbit; and telephone calls and television signals were beamed between Europe and the United States. In 1964, Picturephone service, where customers see and hear one another, was available between New York, Chicago and Washington. In 1965, the Federal Communications Commission launched another major investigation of Bell System policies and services — which is still in progress.

Innovations of all kinds continued, including comprehensive computer systems to handle masses of records and requests, and to print directories without type; international customer-dialed calls in 1966; "voice-prints" found to be as unique to individuals as fingerprints, for crime detection; high-speed teletypewriters which sprayed electronically controlled jets of ink to form letters; and cables made from aluminum to counter the effects of recurring copper shortages.

1969: July 21, Astronaut Neil Armstrong steps out on the moon. Longest telephone call placed from the White House to the lunar surface, over 230,000 miles.

In 1967, H. I. Romnes, a thoughtful and humane engineer born in Wisconsin, became chairman, after heading the Western Electric Company. One of his first ceremonial acts was the presentation of a gold telephone, with push buttons instead of a dial, to President Johnson. *It was the 100 millionth phone in the United States. More than 3 million stockholders now had their savings in the company.* Romnes would be the first business

Since 1920, almost 2500 Theodore N. Vail Awards have been given in tribute to Bell System people who bravely displayed "courage, initiative, good judgement", resourcefulness and accomplishment" for their community's benefit. Usually awarded to individuals for selfless, life-saving efforts, an uncommon exception was made in 1961 *and* 1967 when Vails were given to *all* employees of the Southwestern Bell company for restoring service after natural disasters. Covering an enormous geographic area frequently stricken by floods, tornadoes, duststorms, and hurricanes, Southwestern Bell has an extraordinary record in giving generous aid to the recovery of the many communities they serve as well restoring telephone service quickly, often at great personal risk to workers.

Louis Edward Willett, Medal of Honor winner, 1968. While on military leave from the New York Telephone Company, Private Willett was killed in Vietnam protecting the withdrawal of his squad under fire. Mortally wounded himself, Private Willett was posthumously awarded the Medal of Honor for his "unselfish acts of bravery ... saving [his comrades'] lives at the cost of his own." In tribute to his memory, the New York Telephone Company established a scholarship fund. Thousands of Bell System men and women have served in the Armed Forces during every American conflict, from 1898 to the present.

F.R. Kappel talking via Telstar I satellite with then Vice President Lyndon B. Johnson, seen on monitor in background.

H.I. Romnes during a Picturephone Conference Call, San Francisco, September 17, 1969.

Southwestern Bell Lineman Douglas Tryon moves through waist-deep muck near the Rio Grande helping to restore telephone service after the ravages of Hurricane Beulah, 1967.

Southwestern Bell Cable Splicer Royal Million "wades" to a telephone in Edinburgh, Texas after Hurricane Beulah, 1967. The Stetson floats better than a hardhat, which is normally required for the job.

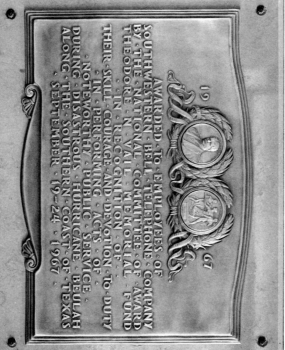

AWARDED TO EMPLOYEES OF SOUTHWESTERN BELL TELEPHONE COMPANY BY THE NATIONAL COMMITTEE OF AWARD THEODORE N. VAIL MEMORIAL FUND IN RECOGNITION OF THEIR SKILL COURAGE AND DEVOTION TO DUTY IN PERFORMING ACTS OF NOTEWORTHY PUBLIC SERVICE DURING DISASTROUS HURRICANE BEULAH ALONG THE SOUTHERN COAST OF TEXAS SEPTEMBER 19-24 1967

Southwestern Bell workers dragging a repair truck through mud following Beulah.

Southwestern Bell Lineman restoring service after a June, 1966 tornado cut a death swath over 15 miles of downtown Topeka, Kansas. Within 72 hours, 18,000 telephones were back in order even though many of the 850 Southwestern Bell people who fixed the damage lost their homes in the tornado's havoc.

10

leader to direct over one million employees and was destined to meet the onslaught of profound doctrinal shifts springing from the nation's changing social values.

ROUGH WATERS: The stream of technical, service and administrative innovations flowed so swiftly and deeply that they came to be taken for granted. Simply listing them makes for tedious reading, and devices and events which would have been frontpage news ten years before were greeted with yawns. Dean Inge's ironic aphorism, "Nothing fails like success," seemed verified monthly. Clashes and anxieties in the country at large manifested themselves in concrete daily problems affecting communications operations. The term "complexity" can be defined as a state of affairs where many important factors in a process all interact with one another, and where the future

outcome of each factor is characterized by uncertainty. This state was — and is — the condition faced by the Bell System and the country since the last decade.

COMPETITIVE FACTORS: As knowledge of communications technology (most of which was developed by the telephone industry) became widespread, entrepreneurs and some regulatory officials saw a new opportunity to introduce competitive elements into an industry whose history had been one of "monopoly regulated by government in the public interest." The venerable policy of total responsibility for service, from every phone to every other, called for total ownership and maintenance of all apparatus involved. Customers bought a *service*, never the equipment itself, and prices were based on overall cost averages. Customers in low cost areas made up for

Map of the Long Lines' switching control areas.

Long Lines installers laying 22 Tube Coaxial transcontinental cable in Nevada, 1973. △

1968 Trimline® Telephone. A 12 button set combining Touch-Tone® features. Two extra buttons are built in for future communications' services.

Long Lines regional network management center (one of ten it operates nationally) produces a rainbow of lights (White Plains, New York). Long Lines operates nearly 400,000,000 circuit miles, 70 per cent in radio relay, 30 per cent in coaxial cable. Bell Laboratories develops the technology and Western Electric manufactures the equipment needed to maintain the circuitry.

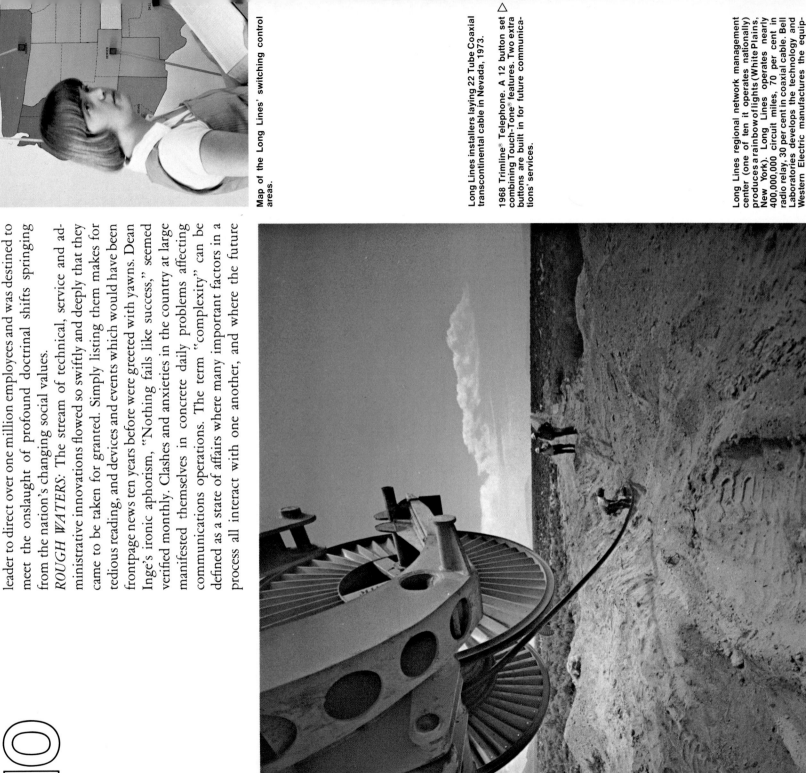

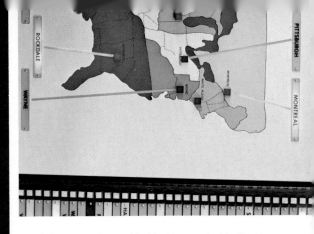

usage and demand caused service deterioration in several large cities. Huge and rapid injections of equipment and personnel trained in accelerated programs were needed before quality levels were restored. The experience showed both how vital telephones had become to modern life (when even persons on welfare were felt to need a phone) and how frustrations with breakdown led to aggressive and hostile behavior.

Vandalism of coin telephones became widespread, and at one time, several hundred were willfully disabled or robbed every weekend in New York. Roving patrols of repairmen are now used to keep them functioning day and night, and most can be used for emergencies without payment, since they are regarded as public safety necessities. Bomb threats to telephone buildings occurred for the first time, and it is melancholy to observe

those in high cost regions, who otherwise could not afford the service. This *social* objective, endorsed for a century by the nation, clashes with the cold dogmas of economic theorems, which were used to justify demands for radical policy changes.

Manufacturers wished to sell phones directly to the public for connection to Bell's lines; promoters of microwave systems received permission to build relay systems paralleling Bell's routes; and satellite ventures were formed to furnish long-distance services by leapfrogging terrestrial facilities. The details of all these controversies are a confusing swamp and thicket of complications, tiresome even to involved specialists. The resulting deluge of litigation and court cases seeking to settle policy for the future is now at full flood.

SERVICE OVERLOAD: In 1969, unprecedented jumps in

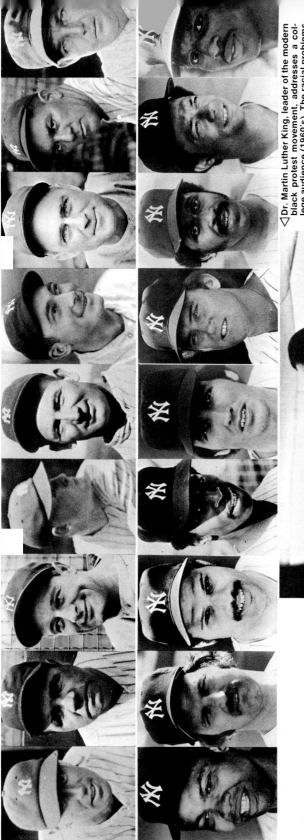

△ Dr. Martin Luther King, leader of the modern black protest movement, addresses a college audience (1960's). The racial problems of America were considered a Southern, regional dilemma until Dr. King made it clear that black discontent was a national condition based on national discrimination. Since his tragic death in 1968, the quality of American black life has improved greatly.

1958 Call Director® Telephone with Touch-Tone® used to handle many incoming, outgoing and inter-office calls simultaneously.
® Registered Trademark of AT&T Co.

Southern Bell's Helen Aiken checking a telephone circuit.

Traffic Operators, 1920's.

Switchman, 1970's.

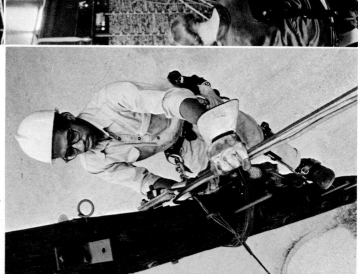

to, and a landmark decision to give economic compensation retroactively was accepted. The Bell System, in effect, was charged with a new responsibility: to *lead* social change rather than to evolve in step with it, as had been thought appropriate throughout its history. Once the command was authoritative and clear, comprehensive administrative programs were instituted for the new role.

FINANCE: For a dozen years before 1969, prices were held down, and for long-distance calls, reduced. But the pressures of inflation and the enormous amounts of new investment to meet demands of customers finally forced applications for increased prices. Each year, the new money needed for construction increased, reaching 4 billion dollars a year by 1972. To induce investors to commit their savings on this scale, the prospective return on their investment had to be raised. Every possible market for funds was tapped with securities designed

that uniformed guards are necessary for protection of a community's communications service.

PERSONNEL: In addition, major strikes took place in 1968. In Illinois, some employees were out 137 days, even during the Chicago presidential convention, which required the use of military units and weapons to control demonstrations in the streets, halls and hotels.

1976: All Nobel Prizes — in Physics, Chemistry, Medicine and Literature — awarded to Americans.

By 1970, the social ferment of the times led the government's Equal Employment Opportunity Commission to challenge Bell System patterns of employment. The business had always been ahead of the nation in antidiscrimination policies, but after lengthy testimony and negotiations, affirmative action programs to increase the proportion of women and minorities in management positions were agreed

10

and sold by Bell's financial forces. Constant involvement in commission hearings across the nation became a way of life, rather than an exceptional expedition for relief. This was, and is, a major challenge to gaining public understanding without parallel.

In 1972, Romnes, aged 65, retired from these exhausting events and labors. He died in the following year.

His successor, John D. deButts, a native of North Carolina, with vast experience in all aspects of the business, gathered the strands of these centrifugal forces to weave a fabric of response to the evolving environment.

THE PRESENT ERA: An admirer of Vail and inheritor of his vision, deButts knew that only by public consent and support could his enterprise carry out the tasks expected by the public. He undertook to clarify goals and develop policies which were grounded on the successful traditions of service responsibility and also adapted to the social changes of the age. Where employees were confused by the intricacies of litigation and attacks, he informed and inspired them; when government officials wished to know his position on an issue, he appeared personally. An accomplished speaker, he made over three hundred addresses in three years, appeared on television programs and met reporters whenever they wished to question him. He developed an attitude directly descended from Vail:

Inform people of all the facts in a controversy, tell them your interpretation and recommendation of what you believe to be in their overall interest, but, let the public decide what they want after being informed by both sides. Then, with the best of cooperation, undertake to deliver it.

In 1973, he made a major address on the competition question at Seattle, where he outlined his policy of full public information and gave an analysis of the ill effects of a contrived competition from artificially segmented markets. He felt that, while some people and organizations would benefit from such competition, the great majority of general customers, especially residences, would be harmed by deterioration of service and higher costs. Their welfare was his main concern. Resolution of *that* question still remains the dominant one on the agenda of national communications policy.

In 1974, the Justice Department instituted another major antitrust action against the Bell System. The issues were venerable, but they were now presented in a turbulent environment. They called for severance of manufacturing, research and the long-distance network operations from Bell System control as a remedy for alleged unjustified dominance of telecommunications. The case may take many years to try, but in a larger sense its outcome should be based on answers to two profound questions for the nation's people:

What kind of country do you want to have? and,

What instruments and methods are needed to achieve it?

In its hundred years, from Vail to deButts, telephone service developed in response to *public desires* coupled to *technical possibilities.* Its future will unfold in the same way, and true determinations of *both* are the only safe beacons by which to navigate its course ahead. □

John D. deButts, who joined the Bell System in 1936, standing at the Control Unit of the New York Telephone Company's Electronic Switching System (ESS) Number One, capable of handling over 110,000 calls in a peak hour. The newest ESS (#4) can handle over 550,000 calls in one hour. Technicians supervising operations are Evelyn Holton and Robert Loughran.

Picturephone® Meeting Service an inter-city visual idea in the 1970's. Cameras are automatically switched to the person speaking. By pressing a button, an electric device delivers a photocopy of whatever picture is being transmitted. Slides, videotapes and printed pages may be sent in seconds. The system is now available between any two of four cities: New York, Washington, D.C., Chicago and San Francisco.

Console Mark 50 PBX introduced in the 1970's, a cordless, push-button office "switching center". Visual signals show status of all lines. △

The story does not end, though this book does. Can we, after a hundred years, discern patterns in the fabric made from an invention, those who allied their lives to its service, and the social development of a growing nation? I believe so.

One lesson is that both the country and the telephone supported each other in realizing their intrinsic potential. Without means of convenient, personal communication, the explosive expansion, both geographical and in sheer population which followed the War Between the States, could not have occurred in ways that allowed all to keep in touch with one another, preserving a national identity under the stress of immense centrifugal forces. That basic, throbbing demand fueled efforts to supply it by visionaries, workers, managers, scientists, engineers and leaders. And the forms they used were those of a business, rather than those of a government bureau.

This was consistent with American values, but the telephone was not an ordinary business. Its leaders did not single-mindedly pursue opportunistic profits, but embraced instead an energizing long-range public service goal. They saw that only by public consent, ratified by government surveillance, could they possibly mobilize the resources needed for the enormous job. (Unlike many other enterprises founded in those days, no great fortunes were amassed by those associated with the telephone.)

Every day, telephone people in the United States visit about 150,000 homes and businesses to perform work and handle, on the average, about six calls from every phone. When one imagines the opportunities such contacts with so many individuals offer for irritation, mishandling and breakdown, it is remarkable how little actually occurs. This unique aggregation

EPILOGUE

of human beings and custom-made hardware, deployed throughout our vast land, performs a service now taken for granted in our country, but which remains the model for the rest of the world, as it has since its beginnings.

Human nature is not perfect, and probably has not changed much since ancient times. Yet an unending stream of human beings have added individual contributions to the culture of communications. Young people, a few months out of school, now operate systems of a complexity that would have been beyond the wildest imagination of their counterparts a generation back, but who *would* have understood that the service goals they support remain the same.

That lesson is indeed relevant to the present antitechnological mood: technology is morally neutral; mankind is not. Technology put at the service of a humane goal will have benign effects; technology which serves degrading goals will produce evils. Telephone technology has been benign; and I believe that happy outcome originated in Vail's humane vision of universal service, and its inheritance by those who volunteered to serve that vision since his day.

In our time, it is fashionable to debunk the accomplishments of our past, and to denigrate those who made them. Certainly they were all human, endowed with those infinite variations of temperament, virtues and faults. Yet I feel that in walking through a garden, one should actually look at and enjoy the flowers, not merely crouch along at ground level in hopes of finding the stray weed. I am old-fashioned enough to think that most people want something to believe in, and to give their energies and intellects to purposeful work in which they can take pride. Of course, a prudent skepticism can keep

one from becoming victimized by illusions and fantasy, but cynicism alone has neither built nor reformed anything worthwhile.

In the story told here, I have concentrated on the high points and events, the dramatic and affirmative steps toward progress. I do not have either space, skill or inclination to "tell everything that happened, including *all the facts*" — that impossible dream of historians in their youth. Instead, my explorations in the parallel lives of the telephone and this country in the last century have brought only confirmation of that age-old wisdom: *Without* vision, the people perish; *with* vision, they have the chance to prosper.

The telephone attracted to its vision of service all aspects of our national temper and regions: there was room for the gregarious and the solitary, those who preferred action and those dedicated to thought, rugged outdoorsmen and sedentary clerks, salesmen and scientists, lawyers and humanists.

Yet all worked together and, in their working, made something indispensable, reliable and beneficial from those ancient building blocks of our civilization: dedicated human effort and that applied knowledge we call technology.

I am proud to have been one of them.

□

Some Sources and Acknowledgements

I have read a great deal of the immense Bell historical materials. Robert V. Bruce's *Bell: Alexander Graham Bell and the Conquest of Solitude* (Boston, 1973) is the definitive biography. Catherine MacKenzie's *Alexander Graham Bell* (Boston, 1928) is a more personal study. Watson's memoirs, *Exploring Life* (New York, 1926) remain a continuous pleasure. For information about Vail, I am indebted to his niece, Katherine Vail Marsters. Kate is my dear friend in whose company I was continually inspired and enlightened about the early days of the business and its people. Albert Bigelow Paine's *Theodore N. Vail* (New York, 1921) is interesting but stiff and dated. It fails to capture the sheer vitality of the man. Vail's *Views on Public Questions*, a collection of speeches and papers on telephony, employs a vigorous prose and sets forth clear ideas which are still relevant. Finally, I used my 30 years acquaintance with telephone business literature, including recent adversary writings, as background for the narrative.

Events in Telephone History, compiled by AT&T's historian, Lewis Gum, was of great value. Photographic librarian Eleanor Romano, gave us our splendid initial base in picture research. Vi Graeper arranged access to historic telephone models. For the general history of the telephone and its times, I visited libraries, historical sites and museums in the United States, Great Britain and Canada, where I was constantly surprised and delighted at the help volunteered for my benefit by their fine staffs. This generous cooperation was also true of photographic archivists in Bell System companies as well as national, state and local historical societies.

Many friends and colleagues, both outside and within the Bell System, kindly helped complete the project. They include: William Albert, Martin Appel, James C. Armstrong, Norman Baxter, Frederick Betts, Stanley Blauser, Edward Bligh, C.F. Boettcher, Chester Burger, Theodore Couch, Jack Fallon, L.L.L. Golden, George Gray, Jack Higgins, Grace Howard, Sandy Hudson, Kay Hurd, Michael Kramer, Helen Kroll, Pat McCallum, James McMahon, Muriel Miller, Roy Moskop, Joseph Mysak, Eileen Noonan, Robert O'Brien, Alfred Parroll, Young Hi Quick, Naseby Rhinehart, Mary Ann Reigel, Richard J. Riley, Leonard Stern, John Stevens, Brian Sullivan, Sal Taiibi, Lori Temple, Muriel Walter, Glenn Watts, Lee White, Robert Wolfenbarger, Thomas Young and Walter Zimmerman.

For American and Comparative history, I enjoyed the sometimes harsh tutelage of my publisher, Gerald Stearn, who once taught both subjects at Columbia University. His designer, Ray Ripper, and his photographer, Richard Steinberg, were founts of creative ideas. Our frenetic collaboration remains a treasured memory. I have tried living in the Cotswolds for a few weeks under mid-nineteenth century conditions. That atmosphere sharpened my sense of what life was like before the communications' revolution.

But without the encouragement, knowledge, taste and wit of my wife, Shirley, this book would not exist.

H.M.B.

Photographic Credits

All color photography is by Richard A. Steinberg, except pictures on the following pages: Bettmann Archive: 25, 27 (2), 28, 29 (2), 30, 33, 35, 37, 46, 76 (bottom left), 79 (2), 81, 100, 101, 103, 125 (2), 173. Western Electric: 19 (2), all illustrations in the Western Electric gatefold (Chapter 7), both color and black & white; and "The Genius of Electricity" opening Chapter 4. AT&T Photographic Archives: 78. Charles L. Brown: 20. Quincy Historical Society: 122. Long Lines Department: 182, 183 (3). Peabody Maritime Museum: 120, 124. All illustrations in the Bell Telephone Laboratories gatefold (Chapter 5), both color and black & white, are from the Bell Telephone Laboratories.

Black & white illustrations: AT&T Photographic Archives: 10, 13, 47 (bottom), 14, 16 (left), 17, 20 (bottom), 21, 36, 38, 49, 50, 52, 60, 67, 76 (top), 78, 83 (all), 85, 86, 87, 89, 94, 95, 96, 100 (top right), 102, 104, 105, 106 (left & right), 107, 108, 109, 112-113 (bottom), 114, 117, 126, 132, 134, 135, 136, 139, 142, 144, 146 (right), 163, 164, 166 (bottom left), 166 (top right), 168, 169, 171, 172, 176, 178-179 (top & bottom), 180 (left), 184 (bottom, left to right).

Bettmann Archive: 15 (right), 26, 28, 31, 32, 33, 34, 42, 45, 57 (right), 81 (left), 90, 97, 99, 100 (bottom right), 112-113 (top), 118, 119, 121 (top left), 120 (bottom right), 128, 130, 140 (bottom), 145, 166 (top left), 167, 170 (left), 172 (top left), 173 (right), 174 (top, left & right), 184 (center). Bell Canada: 47 (top), 136. The Bostonian Society: 48, 15 (left), 56 (right), 121 (top right). Library of Congress (Bell Family Collection): 43, 44, 77, 140 (top), 141, 146 (left), 148, 149, 150, 154, 155, 156, 158, 159, 160. Braintree Historical Society: 55, 120 (right), 121, 122 (right), 134, 135. Essex Institute: 56 (left). Frank Leslie's Weekly: 80, 82. Quincy Historical Society: 124 (right). Vail Family Private Collection: 110, 111, 165, 170-171 (bottom), Archives of the City of Boston: 152-153. New England Telephone & Telegraph Company: 175. Communications Workers of America: 178 (top left, bottom left). New York Telephone Company: 180 (right). Greer Cavegnaro: 181 (bottom right), 181 (top left). Southwestern Bell Telephone Company: 181 (bottom left). Ken Watson: 181 (top right). Milstead Photography: 181 (center). The New York Yankees: 184 (top). The Canadian Sonadisc in the Telephone Pioneer gatefold (Chapter 3) was provided by the Telephone Pioneers of America.

Index

The Making of *The Telephone Book*

Typography: This book was set in 10 on 13 Garamond with display heads in Helvetica Medium by Typographic Art Incorporated, Hamden, Connecticut. Typographic Art was founded in 1964 by two linotype craftsmen, Steven Bachleda and Frederick Lev. Their firm specializes in custom typography for both scholarly and mass-market printing. Copy for the end-sheets was hand-set in foundry type; the text of the book was set using computerized photocomposition.

Paper & Materials: The end-sheets were printed on 80-lb. basis weight Superfine Smooth-White Text paper manufactured by Mohawk Paper Mills, Inc. The dust jackets were printed on 80-lb. basis weight Cameo Dull paper manufactured by the S. D. Warren Company and have been laminated with polypropylene film by the Henschel Company of New Berlin, Wisconsin. All paper stocks were selected in consultation with, and purchased through, Thomas Ferguson of Bulkley Dunton Linde Lathrop of New York City. The 120 Point Binders Board Case was covered in a natural finish, "special order blue" Kingston cloth, manufactured by the Holliston Mills, Inc. The text was printed on 80-lb. basis weight Conso Web Brilliant, manufactured by the Consolidated Paper Company, Inc.

Color Separations, Printing & Binding: All color separations (including halftones), printing and binding were done by the W. A. Krueger Company (WAKCO) in their New Berlin and Brookfield, Wisconsin plants. The book was printed on their #8-25 press in four-color offset. The #8-25 is one of the few printing presses capable of delivering a 9" x 12" text page of high color quality. WAKCO was founded (optimistically) in the dark Depression year of 1934 by, essentially, three printing craftsmen: William A. Krueger, Robert A. Klaus and Harry Quadracci. In over 40 years, WAKCO has become one of the largest Web-Offset color lithographers in the world. Applying 19th century standards of craft excellence to 20th century technology, WAKCO is known for its attention to detail, the creation of a novel method of Web-Offset printing, "Micro-Color"®, and its general printing and binding excellence. WAKCO tested a wide variety of paper stocks and developed the special inks needed to achieve the printing quality of *The Telephone Book.*

® Registered U.S. Patent Office.

NEW ENGLAND TELEPHONE & TELEGRAPH COMPANY THE OHIO BELL TELEPHONE COMPANY THE SOUTHERN BELL TELEPHONE AND TELEGRAPH COMPANY THE SOUTHWESTERN BELL TELEPHONE COMPANY BELL TELEPHONE COMPANY OF PENNSYLVANIA BELL TELEPHONE COMPANY INDIANA BELL TELEPHONE COMPANY ILLINOIS BELL TELEPHONE COMPANY THE CHESAPEAKE AND POTOMAC TELEPHONE COMPANY WISCONSIN TELEPHONE COMPANY THE MOUNTAIN STATES TELEPHONE AND TELEGRAPH COMPANY PACIFIC NORTHWESTERN BELL TELEPHONE COMPANY THE PACIFIC TELEPHONE AND TELEGRAPH COMPANY NORTHWESTERN BELL TELEPHONE COMPANY THE DIAMOND STATE TELEPHONE COMPANY NEW ENGLAND TELEPHONE AND TELEGRAPH COMPANY NEW JERSEY BELL TELEPHONE COMPANY NEW YORK TELEPHONE COMPANY LONG LINES DEPARTMENT THE CHESAPEAKE AND POTOMAC TELEPHONE COMPANY OF VIRGINIA MICHIGAN BELL TELEPHONE COMPANY WESTERN ELECTRIC COMPANY BELL TELEPHONE LABORATORIES CINCINNATI BELL, INC. SOUTHWESTERN BELL TELEPHONE COMPANY AMERICAN TELEPHONE AND TELEGRAPH COMPANY THE CHESAPEAKE AND POTOMAC TELEPHONE COMPANY OF MARYLAND THE CHESAPEAKE AND POTOMAC TELEPHONE COMPANY OF WEST VIRGINIA INDIANA BELL TELEPHONE COMPANY